To Roumiana,

do something amazi[ng]

and measure you[r] , [?]s!

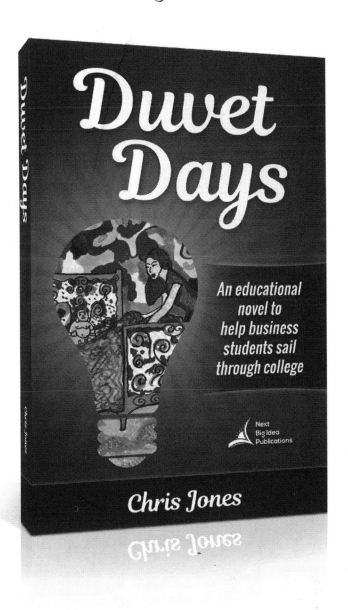

Duvet Days

An educational
novel to
help business
students sail
through college

Next
Big Idea
Publications

Chris Jones

Chris

Published by Next Big Idea Publications.

ISBN 978-0-9574392-1-4

Printed in Great Britain by CreateSpace.

Next
Big Idea
Publications

Praise for Duvet Days

"We need new stories that point to new possible futures - and this book provides them."
Professor Hamish Fyfe, Director, George Ewart Evans Centre for Storytelling

"Chris Jones' business school textbook is extremely creative, blending insightful business management techniques into a fun, readable novel for young adults. Each chapter includes probing questions to stretch minds and develop thinking! At last, a 'Fun to Read' textbook."
Dr James Holt, Emeritus Professor at Washington State University

"The chapters have a wealth of messages to business / entrepreneurial students and cover a number of levels of learning cognitive, social, emotional etc. Using this story telling style delivery provides an opportunity to reflect on many complex and nuanced areas for example corporate social responsibility and how it coexists with profitability, motivation both intrinsic and extrinsic and how this coexists with employability and sustainability, resilience and learning from failure; the list goes on."
Dr Denise Preece, University of Liverpool Management School

"The genius of this book is the way it is written. There were very funny moments. There were chapters where a real person was dealing with real problems. And there were large sections that made me read intensively, as I felt like I was learning with Lucinda."
Scott Caveney, business student at North Wales Business School

"As a Head of Sixth Form, who is always looking to find new ways of embedding learning for students, I think Duvet Days is a fabulous idea. I can see it being used to complement textbooks and teacher notes really successfully and the novel form provides lots of opportunities for independent, student led work. The way that business language is used throughout the narrative, and reinforced in the end of chapter notes, is a very effective way of supporting students' growing understanding of the subject."
Glyn Owen, Head of Sixth Form at Coleshill School

Acknowledgements

To Eli Goldratt, a major inspiration for this book, and the 'Master' of educational storytelling for business.

Special thanks to Anna, Claire and Steph for their support in editing this manuscript.

Credit for the cover design to Bojan and Carmen.

Table of Contents

About the Author

Chris Jones is a Professor and Head of the North Wales Business School, based at Wrexham Glyndŵr University. His career to date has included a PhD in econometrics; six incredible years working for Unilever plc., including a role as European Market Research Manager based in Paris; and four years running his own small business. In 2012, he published his first book, which described the challenges encountered in developing that business – entitled *Selling Moose*.

More recently, he has returned to university life with the simple goal of helping others to attain their own career ambitions. Chris has helped to build a unique and special place for learning about the subject of business, situated on the edge of North Wales. This book is an extension of his philosophy to learning, which is to make it fun and inspiring.

He studied his GCSEs and A-levels at Flint High School, whose most famous former pupil is Jade Jones, the double Olympic *tae kwon do* champion. But learning didn't come easy to him at school, so this book is what he would have liked to read at that time. It's been written for every student out there who needs the subject to be brought to life, in order to make learning easier.

About this Book

Why read this book?

Textbooks can be great for transferring large amounts of relevant information in order to acquire knowledge. This book does not attempt to replace them in any way.

However, not everyone finds it easy to make all that information stick. Thankfully, there is another way to help students understand business – through storytelling. Most of us grew up with stories that began: 'Once upon a time', and we loved them. Stories need to be interesting. Some stories can be funny. Others are sad. But if they are told well, they are memorable. And we learn through memory. That's what Duvet Days attempts to do – educate through the power of the imagination.

The business syllabus for AS/A level, BTEC and foundation year is now more focused upon entrepreneurship and decision-making. Duvet Days is packed full of enterprises and individuals that are all facing decisions – reflecting fully what today's student needs to grasp.

How to study using this book

The 38 chapters of this book tell a number of interweaving stories that should be read in sequence. Unlike textbooks, the business content does not take centre stage, but sits within the story. You will learn as the main character in the books learns. Each chapter concludes with a series of tools to help reinforce the learning and make it stick. As humans, most of us need memory hooks. For example, what do you use to recall the colours of the rainbow? We also need to be reminded of what we've just learnt, and think independently. So do re-visit the sections at the end of each chapter, once you've read the book itself.

What else is available?

There is a website that accompanies this book, packed full of more stuff. This includes exam tips; new scenarios presented as podcasts and case studies; plus some topics not covered in the book. Its domain name is:

StudyBusiness.co.uk

Prologue

Hey! My name is Lucinda Lopez-Lawson, which I guess might make me one of the few people in the world with the initials "LLL". The Lopez bit is my South American Dad, but he's no longer around. So it's just me, Mum and my irritating little brother Jake. And this is my story of how I went from frustrated teenager to … slightly less frustrated grown-up with a future firmly set in the business world. Move over Alan Sugar, you old-timer, I'll kick butt on any reality TV contract you want to send my way!

Why am I writing this book? Well about two years ago, a series of events happened that well and truly changed my life. I had no plans to share them, but then I met a guy – you know how it works, boy meets girl, girl meets boy and boy convinces girl to come and do some guest teaching. But more on that later. And then I figured: why not share my story with a few more people – so here we are, me and you around an imaginary camp fire, with me being chief story-teller. ☺

So this is where it all began. I was eighteen and it was a Sunday. Mum had gone to meet someone. She said it was work-related, but I had my suspicions. If it was someone from a dating site, I just hoped it wasn't Tinder! I was given a list of chores to do and number three on the list was changing the sheets on my bed and that of my brother. Ugh! I seriously hated that job with a passion. Why did I have to touch the sheets of a rank pre-pubescent teenager who clearly dribbles in his sleep, based on the strange patches on his pillow? I didn't dare look for any patches anywhere else!

I'd start with my own bed so I didn't contaminate my own space with any foreign bodies I collected from his. Figuring out which way the sheet needed to go on was the first irritating bit. It's clearly a rectangle, but the difference in length of the two sides is so marginal that to the naked eye, it's impossible to tell which way around it goes. And since I am certifiably the unluckiest person alive, I always chose the wrong way! So just as I was trying to put down the final corner, it wouldn't quite stretch.

iv

Yet that was nothing to the biggest headache – the duvet cover! Firstly, you have to wrestle the big thick duvet through the thin gap at the bottom of the cover. Then you have to make sure you locate both corners of the duvet and match them with the corners of the cover. I've lost track of the number of times I've mislaid a corner in there and had to start all over again. Then, and only then, do you have to engage in a monumental shaking exercise to coax the other end of the duvet into the cover! This particular weekend was where it all came to a head. As I was in the eye of the duvet shaking storm, the whole thing sailed too close to my bedside table and knocked onto the floor one of my most treasured possessions. It was a miniature porcelain Buddha, given to me by my cousin when she was battling cancer. The figure smashed into three pieces. I lay there and sobbed whilst assembling the three pieces back together, thinking of Alicia and all she had gone through.

It was as I emerged from my despair, returning to the mess of a half-completed and badly fitted duvet, that it hit me. Surely there had to be an easier way than this? Am I seriously the only person in the world today that has a weekly fight with a duvet cover? How many other precious items are being swept from bedside tables by the menace that is a three-sided duvet cover enclosure? Wouldn't it make far more sense if, instead of threading the duvet through one pokey opening, you could open the cover up by three sides, lay the duvet on top and then close the other three sides with press-studs or buttons or something? Yes, it would undoubtedly be easier, and no precious bedside items would be harmed in the making of it.

I got out my notepad of ideas, a Christmas present bought for me by my Mum in recognition of the fact I was always coming up with new inventions, and started to draw. In truth, it didn't take much time and effort – just a duvet cover that opens on three sides instead of one. I liken it to a baguette that you slice open, but keep intact at the edge. Once you add your filling, a duvet in this case, you simply fold over the top baguette flap, and *voilà*!

Then I had the trauma of making my brothers bed. Only this time, I went in with renewed vigour, as I was about to prove my theory one more time. His was a single bed, which made the task of threading the duvet through harder still. It was easier to locate the two ends, but a duvet shaking exercise was futile since the whole thing was too narrow, so it needed to be threaded through by hand. Five minutes later, I had justified the case for a new style of duvet cover. No broken precious Buddha figures and a whole lot less fiddling and frustration.

Was this the invention I'd always believed I could conjure up to change the world? Granted, I hadn't expected to make my mark on humankind through a new concept in bed linen. But then, was the inventor of the tin opener not slightly nonplussed that their place in history would be constrained to getting food out of cans? Of course not. And neither should I care about mine. The bigger challenge that confronted me was where on earth should I go with this next?

CHAPTER 1

Seriously?

When my Mum returned from her *rendezvous* a few hours later, along with my brother, her surprise to see me bounding down the stairs, grinning broadly, was justified.

"Well, what have I done to deserve such a happy daughter?"

"Hey Mum! How was your 'meeting'?" I beamed as my brother shot up the stairs to his room, without so much as a look. "Hello to you too, dwarf," I shouted.

"Not as good as your afternoon by the look of things. I haven't seen a smile like that since you won that race at Sports Day."

"Mum, that must have been like eight years ago! Life's not been that bad since under your management. But as it happens, I have had a surprisingly good day."

"That's good to know. Put the kettle on whilst I get changed and you can tell me all about it."

I proceeded to explain my day over two cups of tea, whilst she prepared dinner. How I completed all the chores she had drawn up. Then I introduced my usual duvet battle and the discovery of a much better solution.

"I agree it's a pain, which is why I give it to my favourite daughter to do for me!"

"Mum, I'm your only daughter. So what do you think of my much better idea?"

"It sounds wonderful darling. Now you've just got to convince the world's duvet cover companies to see sense."

"But that's it Mum, what if I don't and do it myself instead?"

"Make a duvet cover?! You've never sewed in your life, my love."

"I'm not talking about me making it, Mum. And I'm not talking about making just one. What I'm saying is, I think I've stumbled on a great business idea here."

"A business idea? Oh I'm not sure about that."

"But Mum, you agreed it makes total sense! I think this could be my *eureka moment*. You remember we watched that TV programme last week where the good-looking entrepreneur guy said everyone has at least one genius idea inside them? Well I really think this is mine!"

"I just think there must be a reason why they are not making them that way already."

"It's probably easier and cheaper for them, but that doesn't mean it's right for the people who have to use them. And anyway, maybe nobody has thought of it?"

"Maybe someone has thought of it, Lu. Have you tried Googling it?"

"No not yet, I've only just finished all the jobs you gave me. I'm not sure what I would stick into Google. If someone has done it, how come we've never seen them in shops that way?"

"Well, there is that I suppose."

"So you agree I should go for it? Will you support me?"

"I never said that. I don't see how you could possibly break into an industry like that. They've got it all sewn up. Ha, all sewn up, get it?!"

"Yeah Mum, hilarious. But nowadays lots of people start businesses small and build them up. That's what I could do. I could promote it on social media for a start."

"There's a bit more to it than that, darling. How are you going to make them for a start? And get the money together to generate all the stock? Something like that is going to need finance we haven't got and connections we don't have."

"I should have guessed you'd be negative, Mum! You never support anything I want to do."

"Lu, that's not true! I just think it sounds like something we could never do. And for what it's worth, I do like your idea."

"Well don't be so defeatist then. Help me figure out how to try and do something good with my life."

"Darling you will do something good with your life. You're eighteen and have got your whole life ahead of you, which I know will be a complete success. But first, you need to get through college, maybe go to university and then get a job."

"But what if that's not what I want to do? It might be what you want me to do, but that doesn't make it right for me."

"You know I'll support you with whatever you decide to do, but this idea sounds out of our depth."

"We don't know till we try, Mum."

"Well why don't you ask a few more people first – see what others think?"

"But if I tell a load of people, one of them will end up stealing the idea."

"Alright. At least start with Steve. You can trust him and he knows about setting up businesses. Plus, you know he'll give you an honest opinion."

Steve is my Uncle and one of my Mum's two brothers. She had a point. Uncle Steve and I always got on well and he is a lot less cautious than my Mum. He had set up his own consultancy in Business Analytics a few years earlier, and it was doing really well.

"Good idea Mum. I'll text him now and tell him to expect me tomorrow." I got up to go and find my phone.

"Maybe he could buy into the business if he likes it?" Mum said quickly as I left the room. It was evident she felt guilty for being less than enthusiastic.

"Yeah maybe," I replied coolly.

I texted my Uncle and got a reply two minutes later to say he'd treat me to a posh coffee in town after work. It would be a chance to escape my Aunt Kath for an hour.

What you've covered:

Theme	Amplification
Enterprise	Understand the reasons why people start businesses
Decision-making	Explain the purpose of Business Analytics

Memory hook: Seriously?

The response Lucinda gets from her Mum is typical of others who hear new business ideas. Many people are cautious and risk-averse by nature. The challenge of would-be entrepreneurs is to evaluate whether the reasons people give for their ideas not working can be overcome, or are ill-founded.

So, key points to remember:

- People can start businesses for many reasons, often in combination. These include:

1. They want the opportunity to make money.
2. The lifestyle of 'being their own boss' is appealing.
3. They want to make a difference - socially, environmentally etc.
4. They enjoy taking risks.
5. They have an idea they are passionate about pursuing.

- Business Analytics involves collecting and interrogating data in order to support business decision-making. A good example of this is the way supermarkets collect data from customers using loyalty cards.

Now ask yourself:

Why the likes of Elon Musk, Richard Branson, Jo Malone and Mark Zuckerberg started their businesses.

Now ask yourself (suggested answers):

Why the likes of Elon Musk, Richard Branson, Jo Malone and Mark Zuckerberg started their businesses.

Elon Musk co-founded PayPal. When eBay acquired it for $1.5 billion, he received a $165 million share. Musk has since gone on to launch a series of other businesses, which include Tesla and Solar City. Technology is a consistent theme throughout his ideas. However, he would say that the profit from PayPal has enabled him to follow his passion for science and doing things to benefit the world and humanity. His energy is focused upon creating extraordinary solutions such as spaceflight and pioneering energy projects, rather than making money.

Richard Branson's first venture was a youth-culture magazine. However, his ultimate passion was music and he used the success of his magazine to start Virgin Records. He is well known for his risk-taking and adventurous approach to business and life. Branson suffers from dyslexia and had struggled at school due to a lack of awareness and empathy of the condition at the time. This suggests a key motivation for him starting out in business could have been the challenge of doing things that people believed he wasn't capable of.

Like Branson, Jo Malone also suffered from dyslexia in her childhood and left school without any qualifications. She initially worked as a facial masseur, but hit on the idea of providing her clients with bath oil concoctions as a token of appreciation. Her talent for mixing different scents to create unique fragrances enabled her to start her own store – Jo Malone London, which she later sold to Estée Lauder. Jo was raised in modest surroundings, yet this didn't prevent her passion and talent for business emerging: "I love creating something and making someone want to buy it. I am a merchant at heart."

Mark Zuckerberg's business acumen seems to have been founded upon his talent for computer programming and devising ways of putting this to use. He developed numerous computer projects throughout his teenage years. Zuckerberg has demonstrated single-mindedness and astute decision-making on when to accept offers of investment, and when to turn others down. It is alleged he received numerous offers for Facebook, yet could see its greater potential and so rejected each one. In doing so, he became one of the world's richest men.

CHAPTER 2

The snack's in the post

"I just don't know why she couldn't be a bit more positive, that's all! Just a little bit of encouragement." I was sat with Uncle Steve in Starbucks over a giant vanilla latte and having a whinge about Mum.

"Don't be hard on her Lulu, she's just thinking of you in a funny sort of way." Uncle Steve had called me Lulu all my life. He used to say I was like New York – so good they should name me twice.

"It was the same when I was doing that school design competition and she talked me out of what I wanted to do because she said I was being too ambitious. If I'd stuck with it, I'd have won for sure!"

"It's natural for people to look for reasons why something won't work, particularly if they care about you. The secret is to either provide a counter-argument that addresses their concerns, or agree and come up with a workable solution."

"Is that what you did with your business?"

"Kind of yes. Your Aunt was concerned about the loss of our guaranteed income. But over the years, I'd built up a strong network of contacts, so when the time came to go it alone, I knew I could take some of them with me as clients. Without them, I would never have convinced *the dragon* to let us do it."

"Ha, one of these days I'll tell Aunt Kath you call her *the dragon*, if you're not careful!"

"Stand well back when you do, or the flames will engulf you! So, what is this wonderful idea of yours, anyway?"

I repeated the same story I'd told Mum. He listened intently, aside from an intense grimace when I mentioned making my brother's bed.

"I dread to think what you could find in that boy's bed, Lulu!"

"Don't even go there, Uncle Steve." I paused hesitantly, hoping for a positive look. "So? What do you think?"

"Well it's not a surprise, you've always been a great problem solver. What do I think of it as a business idea?"

"Yes."

"It ticks certain boxes. It's innovative and clearly creates a solution for anyone who finds making a bed the traditional way a pain in the butt. It would be easy enough to make a prototype. And it should be possible to make a profit from doing it. But then you need to ask yourself some questions. Has it not been done before? Or even is it being done now? So have you done a web search to see what is currently out there? It could be that someone is doing it already but it just hasn't filtered into the mainstream."

"I should have checked last night. Shall I get it on my phone now?"

"No, leave that until you get back. How all you youngsters can search the web on a tiny screen like that is beyond me!" Uncle Steve was still in the dark ages when it came to smartphones, which is hilarious for someone who has built a successful business using IT.

"You need to do proper market research before you go any further, Lulu."

"But doesn't that involve going out and interviewing loads of people?"

"Not necessarily. Market research involves gathering and analysing data and there's two ways to do it. Primary research is what you are thinking of. It means asking people for their opinions on stuff. It used to be done by people with clipboards in the high street or phoning people up when they're about to eat their tea. But now people don't shop on high streets and they put the phone down on cold callers. So it's better done online through websites or social media."

He took a slurp of coffee, so I waited for him to continue.

"The challenge with primary research is it needs to be done properly in order to be useful. You need to select the right people, and the right number of people; otherwise it could lead to bias. So, for example, you know you get those healthy snacks sent to you through the post?"

"Yeah, Graze."

"Well, it's no good asking people like me about whether I'd want that. For a start, do I look like I'm into healthy snacks?" He patted his paunch. "And even if I were, I'd just go out to the shop and buy some. So to research an idea like that, you need to ask people who might want healthy snacks delivered to their door."

"But what if you interview a bunch of people who want something strange that no one else wants?"

"Exactly. That's why you need to ask lots of people so you don't get influenced by a small section of the market. But then, asking lots of people can be costly and time consuming."

"So probably not right for me then?"

"Maybe, but not initially. To begin with, secondary research is what you need to do. This means finding information that is already out there. So figuring out what other companies are doing in the world of bedding would be a good start. These are your competitors after all."

"So what do I put into Google?" I asked.

"It's about putting duvet covers on more easily, right? So try something like 'easy duvet cover'. See what comes of that and then try other words based on what comes up. But it's not quite that easy."

"How do you mean?"

"Well, because of two things. Firstly, you've got to consider the competition a bit more widely than just other people doing your idea. They are your direct competition. But you've also got indirect competition, which I guess is the traditional duvet cover manufacturers. Beyond indirect competition, you also have substitutes. For example, there may be products on the market to make putting a duvet cover on more easy, that doesn't involve a new duvet cover design."

"I can't imagine what that could be? Whichever way you cut it, you have to feed that duvet in and then hope you locate all the corners."

"You'll be surprised what weird inventions people come up with. Even weirder than yours!"

"Hey, you can go off people you know!"

"Substitutes might be a different type of product, but they are still capable of taking market share away from you. So, coming back to your healthy snacks. What if the solution isn't mailing them healthy snacks but instead mailing them the seeds to grow their own healthy snacks? Then you have a whole different business idea, but potentially for the same set of customers."

"That would never work!"

"Ten years ago, I'd have said snacks through the post would never work too!"

"OK, and that's a substitute? I get it. And the second thing?"

"Uh? Oh yeah, the second thing is intellectual property, which is all about protecting ideas. There are four types of intellectual property. You've got trademarks, but that's just big companies protecting their brand name. Then you've got copyright, which covers logos and stuff like creative material, such as songs or videos. Then there are trade secrets, like the secret recipe for Coca-Cola. Finally, there's a patent and that's the thing you might need to worry about."

"Patent. I've heard of that before, but never been sure what it means."

"A patent is basically a kind of protection for a new product design that is innovative. I guess what you are proposing to do is innovative and therefore it could be that someone has filed a patent on it."

"How would I know if they had? And would it then stop me doing it?"

"There are lots of patent offices around the world. You'd need to check with the UK patent office first. But people can file a patent in another country and pay to have it protected worldwide. So if someone has already patented it and then find out that you have started making them, then technically they could sue you."

"Is it likely that someone would have done that?"

"You never know. Some people file a patent for something but then never set about doing it themselves. Perhaps they wait for people to do it and then use their patent to stake a claim on their business. It's unlikely, but you'd be better off checking. I'm sure there will be a local patent officer who can help, but the first thing is to go and check if anyone is already making them."

"Thanks for that. It sounds a bit scary. Do you think I should bother with this?"

"What have you got to lose? At the very least, it will satisfy your curiosity. And if someone is doing it, then at least I know what to buy you for Christmas!"

"Ha! Make sure you buy one for my stupid brother too, because I'm his *Chief Bed Maker* as well!"

"A duvet cover for Christmas? I'm not sure he'd thank me for that! Right are we done? Do you want to pop back – your Aunt Kath was baking your favourite marshmallow cookies when I left."

"Do I ever!"

What you've covered:

Theme	Amplification
Enterprise	Explain the characteristics of a good business idea
Market research	What is meant by market research
Market research	Distinguish between primary and secondary research
Market research	The value of carrying out market research
Marketing	Direct competition, indirect competition and substitutes
Enterprise	The role of intellectual property in protecting a business

Memory hook: The snack's in the post

Think of the discussion they had around a business delivering snacks through the post. Planning a business like this requires market research around the type of people who might buy this product (segmentation). The business may have direct competition (other online snack retailers), but also indirect competition (e.g. supermarkets) or a substitute product (e.g. 'grow your own').

So, key points to remember:

- Business ideas need to:
1. Satisfy a need - in this case, making it easier to change duvet covers.
2. Be achievable - for Lucinda, can a prototype be made, etc.?
3. Be well researched - identify what else is being done and by whom.
4. Be financially viable – can it make a profit at some point in the future?

- Market research is about gathering and analysing data through:
    - Primary research: asking people questions relating to the product or service directly. To avoid bias, the people selected need to be representative of a typical customer. This can be costly and difficult.
    - Secondary research: studying what others have already found out. This is easier to do, but the data could be misleading or out of date.
- Direct competitors sell the same product or service to the same set of customers. Indirect competitors are in a different market, but may still sell the product or service. Substitutes are an alternative way of solving the same problem.
- Intellectual property falls into four main categories: trademarks, copyright, trade secrets and patents.

Now ask yourself:

1. Many new companies like Google, Facebook and Amazon have taken years to make a profit. Why was this and did this make them bad businesses?
2. When designing a market research survey, what types of issues/questions should you be exploring?
3. What sort of indirect competition exists for a theme park?
4. Can you provide one example for each of: a trademark, a copyright, a trade secret and a patent?

Now ask yourself (suggested answers):

1. **Many new companies like Google, Facebook and Amazon have taken years to make a profit. Why was this and did this make them bad businesses?**

   Some online businesses do not generate any income for the first few years. Instead, they focus on building up a base of loyal users and banking on payback in the long-term. It is investors who principally finance them. For example, Google spent its formative years simply offering its free search engine. Revenue from Google Adwords came later. However, it was steadily acquiring its global base of dedicated users. Amazon, meanwhile, has always operated on a low margin business model. Both strategies made it unrealistic for them to make short-term profit.

2. **When designing a market research survey, what types of issues/questions should you be exploring?**

   a. Is the person being surveyed representative of the target market?
   b. Are they buying the product/service for them or someone else?
   c. What are their reasons for buying?
   d. Have they considered other options? If so, which?
   e. Who do they consult before buying? Friends, media, experts?
   f. Is this their first purchase experience?
   g. Where and when are they buying? E.g. online versus in-store; time of day, time of week, time of year?
   h. What are their future intentions around this product/service?

3. **What sort of indirect competition exists for a theme park?**

   Theme parks are typically aimed at two demographics: families and groups of young people. Alternative activities might therefore include: zoos, days at the beach or in the park, country shows, leisure centres, sports events and entertainment such as concerts or cinema. Theme parks are not considered 'educational', so anything that promotes the combination of education and fun will hold an advantage for parents.

4.   **Can you provide some examples for each of: a trademark, a copyright, a trade secret and a patent?**

Trademark:
Most big companies have trademarked their brand, such as Google, Amazon and Apple.

Copyright:
Creative work like books (such as this one), music lyrics, movies and photos will be subject to copyright.

Trade secret:
Well-known trade secrets in the food industry include soft drink recipes such as Coca-Cola and Dr Pepper, plus KFC's '11 herbs and spices'. The Google search algorithm is heavily protected and is therefore a trade secret.

Patent:
Items such as the electric motor, the first machine for slicing bread, the aeroplane and the light bulb have all been patented at some point. Many new inventions today will be going through the same process.

CHAPTER 3

Read all about it!

The cookies were amazing as usual. I sat with my Aunt and Uncle in their kitchen demolishing them whilst discussing my idea. They were curious to know whether being an entrepreneur was something I wanted to pursue beyond finishing college.

"I suppose I've always enjoyed coming up with new ideas. And I am prepared to work hard at anything I believe in. Isn't that enough?"

"Lots of people have different views on what are important," said Uncle Steve. "Many believe it's about taking risks, but most successful entrepreneurs take calculated risks."

"I think you have to be very single-minded," added Aunt Kath. "You have to know what you want and pursue it relentlessly. I certainly think that fits with you *Honey*, you are very tenacious."

"Plus, you need to have good, basic business sense. Most entrepreneurs in my network are superb salesmen."

"And saleswomen!" cut in Aunt Kath, cutting my Uncle an acerbic look.

"Yes and women. They need to communicate their vision in a way that inspires others. And they need to understand the figures and negotiate hard. You have to be pretty cold-blooded about it."

I felt puzzled by this. "But aren't we now in an age where people are being more ethical and have a social conscience?"

Uncle Steve shook his head. "No, I think you misunderstand me. I'm not saying you can't be good and moral in business. It's just, when it comes down to it, everyone wants to get the best deal they can – whether you are the customer or the supplier. People will try to bargain with you and you will need to know your margins, otherwise you could end up losing money on a deal."

"So there's about six qualities you would need from the Oracle there," said Aunt Kath sarcastically, "but I think the most important thing is that you need to believe in what you are doing. And if it turns out that this idea of yours is something you truly believe in, then you should go for it and we will support you."

"Thanks," I replied gratefully. "But I guess the next thing I need to do is the secondary research you spoke about?"

"Definitely," said Uncle Steve. "And if it's still worth pursuing beyond that, then we'll need to consider planning it all out."

"A business plan you mean?"

"Not necessarily a full blown plan at this stage. Just a roadmap on what needs to be done, so that when you go and speak to some people, you have something to work from. Business plans are important if you have to go and sell your idea to a potential investor, like a bank manager. But they are also important to help owners understand where they are going and what steps need to be taken."

"So what sort of things will I need in my plan?"

"Well a good summary of the business and why you are doing it. An understanding of the market you are entering, which you will have once you do your market research. An insight into the skills of the people in the business and also areas they need to develop. Most importantly of all, financial forecasts for the business going forward."

"Sounds like a lot of things I need to work out then."

"You just need to make sure you really understand what you are getting into. I remember going to speak to a business advisor when I first thought of starting my business. She asked lots of questions which I hadn't thought about and I felt a complete imbecile."

"Fancy a female business advisor running rings around you!" said Aunt Kath mockingly. "Who would have thought we know anything about business, Lu?!"

"Alright, I'm beginning to feel ganged up on here. I know when it's time to go and watch the football."

"One more thing," I asked. "Just so I haven't got the wrong end of the stick. When you keep talking about 'markets', you mean the industry I'm selling into, right?"

"Kind of yes, but specifically about your potential customer base. So, let's think of an example … alright, nowadays all the newspapers around tube stations in London are pretty much given away for free, aren't they? But not so long ago, there were actually newspaper vendors based around tube stations, making a living by selling their newspapers. So they would be in the retail industry, yes? But they were only selling to people who needed a newspaper in that area. So if they were situated in the financial district, they'd need to stock more copies of the Financial Times. A newspaper seller in a less affluent suburb might have needed fewer copies of that paper and more of the Sun or the Mirror. See? It's the same industry, but different markets."

"I think I get it. So people selling health snacks through the mail are selling to the entire country, but specifically to people with an interest in healthy snacks?"

"Exactly. But if you sold the same snacks on one particular high street, then the whole country is not going to visit your shop. Customers will just be locals or tourists. But they will still be the same kind of people."

"Got it. Well, thanks for listening and helping," I said gratefully. "I suppose I'd better head back. It sounds like I've got a fair bit of work to do."

"I'll run you around," said Uncle Steve. "Gives me a chance to tell that sister of mine how proud she should be of her daughter."

I hugged my Aunt Kath and set off home, stealing one last cookie on my way out.

What you've covered:

Theme	Amplification
Enterprise	The characteristics of an entrepreneur
Business plans	The purpose and importance of a business plan, and the components that go into it
Markets	What is meant by a 'market'

Memory hook: Read all about it!

Remind yourself of the newspaper seller outside a tube station to understand the concept of a market. It's one industry, but there are lots of different markets across London. If they get their order quantities wrong, they won't maximise their sales. To survive in that sort of business they would need to appreciate their market and calculate the number of papers they need to sell each day to make a living. For a business like that, primary research might be as simple as observing how many pedestrians pass by over the course of a day.

So, key points to remember:

- An entrepreneur will typically have the following traits and skills:
1. **Creative** in spotting new opportunities or finding a fresh perspective on an existing idea.
2. **Single-minded** and determined - believe in what they are doing.
3. Have **good business sense**, particularly understanding basic financial calculations.
4. Able to **communicate** with passion and persuasion.
5. An appreciation of **risk** - distinguishing 'good' risks from 'bad' risks.
6. Good **sales and negotiation skills**.

- Different markets exist within different industries. Markets can be local or global, online or face-to-face, as well as being aimed at different segments of society.
- A business plan is often written to help sell a business idea to a potential investor. However, it also helps people inside the business to see what needs to be done.

Now ask yourself:

Think about the automotive industry. What markets exist within it? And what features will change from market to market?

Now ask yourself (suggested answers):

Think about the automotive industry. What markets exist within it? And what features will change from market to market?

Some people are satisfied with any car that 'gets them from A to B'. For others, their car satisfies a wider need or desire, which creates different markets. These include:

1. Families: Most people with families base their car purchasing decision around issues of practicality and safety.
2. Rural location: People living in mountainous or 'poor terrain' locations. For example, 4x4s are considered necessary in these areas.
3. High performance cars: Some people are attracted to cars for their speed or their image.
4. Distance travelled: Those people who travel long distances in their cars will prioritise comfort and fuel economy. People who just use their car to drive around town may prefer smaller cars to aid parking and manoeuvrability.
5. Environment: Some see cars as a negative impact on the environment. They may either choose to do away with cars altogether, or purchase one that has low emissions.

Various markets within the car industry have been created to satisfy these needs and preferences. Some differences amongst these markets include:

1. Life cycle - drivers who use their vehicle around town are likely to retain their car for longer than those that travel long distances.
2. Running costs - high performance cars are perceived to be a greater risk, so this will influence other industries such as insurance and parts manufacture.
3. Tax - governments impose higher taxes on cars with a high environmental impact.
4. Interior design – family cars (i.e. 'people carriers') are designed so that the seating layout can be adjusted easily.

CHAPTER 4

A window to the future

The next evening, I embarked on my secondary research.

I started with some online searching that was totally depressing. It appears there is a company already selling duvet covers with my same design! They are called the Easy Lay Duvet Cover Company and seem to be doing exactly what I planned.

I called Uncle Steve to tell him the news and that my game was up. He checked their website and called me back ten minutes later.

"Yes, it seems like they are doing it, but it doesn't necessarily mean the game is up. It comes back to intellectual property. If you were to copy their brand name, then you would have a problem, but going with any other name would be fine."

"So, it's not the end of the world then?" I said desperately.

"No, but it does raise some interesting questions."

"Such as?" I asked.

"Well for a start off, they make no mention of a patent. This means they either haven't thought of patenting the idea or have already checked and someone else has beaten them to it."

"Which one do you think it could be?"

"The only way of knowing would be to do a patent search ourselves. I'll do it later. My guess is they haven't thought of it. There is a bigger worry though."

"What's that?"

"If you look on their news reel, it kind of goes a bit stale from about 2011. Going three years without any updates suggests they are not actively pursuing their business. Plus, when you try to purchase something, all of their product lines are 'temporarily out of stock'."

"That's good news isn't it? It means they are not serious competitors."

"Well yes, there is that," said Uncle Steve. "But you need to think of it another way. Why are they no longer actively in business? What has happened that has prevented it taking off?"

"Maybe they had some personal problems. They seem to be a couple."

"Possibly. Or perhaps they just weren't able to make the business idea work. Perhaps there wasn't enough demand out there for the product."

"So you think it's a bad idea?"

"No, I'm not saying that. I just think you always need to ask why a business has failed or is failing. Some entrepreneurs see the problem, then take over or copy the struggling business and make a success of it by doing what the other company hadn't seen. That could be the case here. However, it should be a warning sign."

"Their website looks OK I guess, but it could be improved."

"Yes I agree. Although the quality of the website shouldn't matter if they are getting the message out. I checked their social media links and they go to an individual rather than a company. I'm guessing the business wasn't given their total focus. Perhaps it was a project that fizzled out."

"So, where does that leave me?"

"Well, I would return to your research and look a bit deeper. I must admit that after taking you home last night, I did a bit of searching myself, except I went on Amazon. I actually found a product that might interest you. It's a clip you can buy to help align the duvet to the corners of the duvet cover."

"So, is that an example of indirect competition, or a substitute?"

"I'd say it's an example of a substitute product. Something that you can buy to solve the problem you have identified, but in a different way to you."

"Sounds like it doesn't avoid the problem of wrestling with the duvet cover though. Aligning the corners is actually the easy bit. You would still have to get the duvet into the corners."

"Yes, but it retails for about three quid. So it attempts to solve the problem for next to nothing."

"Hmm, still not sure I should be worried by that. You still have to buy a duvet cover in the first place."

"Look, I'll check out the patent for you. What I suggest you do is go off and learn more about the duvet cover industry. Who are the top five retailers and who are the top five manufacturers? What are their price-points and what are their features?"

"Price-points?"

"The price they sell for. You should also do a social media trawl to see what is being said about duvet covers. Can't imagine you'll get much out of it other than some celebrity gossip about who is sleeping with who, but you never know until you try."

"Sounds like a lot of tedious web searching to me."

"Well, being an entrepreneur's not all red carpets and champagne, Lulu! You need to know your industry inside out. If you're not prepared to do the legwork then you need to give it up now. Oh and don't forget to write everything down that you find out. Put it into a Word file so it's there electronically once you get to the business plan stage."

"Sure. Thanks for your help, Uncle Steve," I said, slightly embarrassed that I'd shown a lack of enthusiasm.

"One last thing. I've just been reading an interesting article on windowless planes. It's amazing. Above the floor, the entire plane is basically one big window."

I gasped. "Oh my God, that sounds terrifying!"

"It got me thinking about your idea. You might want to check it out and read up about *product features*."

"How do I that?"

"Try putting it into Google and see where it takes you."

Three hours later, I felt like I knew way more about the world of duvet covers than any normal eighteen year old should. Yet I also felt much more comfortable being able to hold a conversation on the subject.

I also did a search on windowless planes and looked up the meaning of *product features*. This meant I started to think about the *tangible product*, the *core benefit* and *augmented benefit*. This was all new to me but hey-ho! So the tangible product is about its key physical features. For me that was surely the innovative design of the duvet cover? The core benefit would then be less time and stress making the bed. The augmented product was harder to define as it was all about extras such as free delivery, extended guarantee or after-sales. Answers on a postcard for that one!

This led me onto a whole load of other stuff that I'd never heard of before, like the *product life cycle*. Well, I was clearly in *development* stage now. But then my product would go through four stages, from *introduction* through to *decline*. At the *introduction* stage I should expect sales to be low and I'd need to find ways of raising awareness. *Growth* seems to be a good stage as that's where it's taking off. *Maturity* is when the product is no longer growing at a fast rate. *Decline* means that sales are falling.

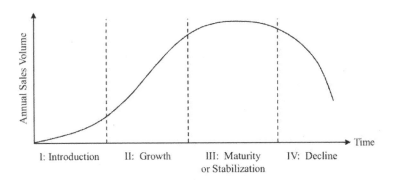

Product Life Cycle Curve.

This cycle seems to change from product to product. So high-tech or fad products go through the cycle fast. Ideas like mine may take longer to enter decline.

Just when I thought I was done, I clicked on a link to the *Boston matrix*. Thankfully, this only seemed to apply to businesses that had lots of products. I only had one. It was still interesting to learn about it though.

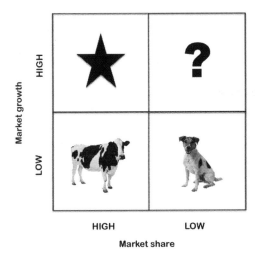

Boston Matrix.

Star products were the ideal: a high share of a high growth market. I thought back to Uncle Steve's newspaper vendors outside tube stations. If you were the only vendor outside a station with new buildings shooting up everywhere, then you were surely a star product. New buildings would mean lots of potential customers about to arrive at your station.

Products with a high share of a market with low growth potential would be categorised as *cash cows*. Heinz tomato ketchup sprung to mind for this.

At the other end of the spectrum was a *dog product*. This was a bad scenario - low market share in a market with low growth potential. So an unfashionable tube station with lots of other vendors then.

Finally, the *question mark* category. This represents products with a more uncertain future: lots of market growth potential, but a low current market share. I imagined this would be where windowless planes currently sit.

So where was my idea? Well I guess the duvet cover market has low growth potential and I'd certainly have low market share. A *dog*! But then, I remembered that the industry is not necessarily the same as a market. So if a new market can be created for easy fitting duvet covers then maybe that changes things? The traditional design of duvet covers would be in the 'decline' phase and mine would be in 'growth', putting me in the *question mark* category. So the challenge was to change people's view of the market.

It was all a bit complicated, but pretty interesting. Now I just needed to find someone that wanted to talk about duvet covers too. Turns out, I was about to meet someone keen to do just that, two days later.

What you've covered:

Theme	Amplification
Marketing	Recall the threat of substitute products as a form of indirect competition
Marketing	The tangible product, the core benefit and the augmented product
Marketing	The stages of a 'product life cycle'
Marketing	The purpose of the 'Boston matrix'

Memory hook: A window to the future

Think of the windowless plane as a product with features and benefits - try putting it in a search engine to get a picture of it. Now consider its product life cycle. It's currently in development phase. Recall the stages it will go through. If you need help remembering the five stages, just memorise the initials - 'Dig MD'. Say it a few times and it will stick.

So, key points to remember:

1. When marketing a product, it's important that businesses understand its key features and the benefit to the customer.
2. As well as key features and benefits, the augmented product refers to the *extras*. For example, Amazon places a lot of emphasis on its easy *returns policy*.
3. Products can grow in two ways. Firstly, the overall market for the product can grow - such as the growth in smartphones. Secondly, a product can outperform the market. A good example of this is Minecraft, which has easily outperformed the children's computer games market.
4. The Boston matrix helps to show where certain products sit in terms of these two criteria - the growth of the market itself and their share of that market.
5. All different types of product have different life cycles. Businesses try to maximise the time spent in the growth and maturity phases.

Now ask yourself:

1. Consider the 'Rolex' brand. How would you describe its core benefit, the tangible product and the augmented product?
2. Imagine the following product types: electric cars, a child's toy from the hit movie 'Frozen', iced lollies and smartphones. Try drawing the product life cycle curve for each of these types.
3. The energy drink market is predicted to grow by 55% from its annual global sales of 2013 to the year 2021. In 2013, Red Bull held a 43% market share. Coca-Cola has introduced its own product into this market with a drink called 'Full-throttle'. Its market share in 2013 was just 1%. Where would you place these two products on the Boston matrix?
4. The windowless plane is predicted to be the future of aircraft. What is the main barrier that will hinder its growth?

Now ask yourself (suggested answers):

1. **Consider the 'Rolex' brand. How would you describe its core benefit, the tangible product and the augmented product?**

    Tangible product: a reliable and high quality watch that tells time accurately.

    Core benefit: its style and image makes it an exclusive fashion statement. Equally, Rolex promote their longevity in the market to reassure customers of their status and permanence. For example, their current strapline around sports events is "we don't just tell time, we tell history". This also fits with their focus on quality – their products are built to last.

    Augmented product: aside from their brand image, Rolex also offer high-end guarantees on quality. This includes a five-year warranty and a ten-year service recommendation. These timescales are favourable compared to most of their rivals.

2. **Imagine the following product types: a child's toy from the hit movie 'Frozen', iced lollies and smartphones. Try drawing the product life cycle curve for each of these types.**

    A child's toy is a good example of a *fad* product, one that has high short-term demand but then drops quickly as interest wanes and new products emerge. Occasionally, these products will come back into fashion in future generations.

    An iced lolly is more likely to be in high demand during the summer months. In the winter, demand is likely to be low. This is a seasonal product so the life cycle curve will look wave like.

    Smartphones have gone through a huge growth period as most people around the world have got on board. They are therefore an example of a *boom* product. Eventually, the market will reach a peak. However, it sustains itself by offering new models with improved features. In time, the market may recede as new innovations take over.

The product life cycle curves for these different scenarios would look something like this:

A fad product   A seasonal product   A boom product

3. **The energy drink market is predicted to grow by 55% from its annual global sales of 2013 to the year 2021. In 2013, Red Bull had a 43% market share. Coca-Cola has introduced its own product into this market with a drink called 'Full-throttle'. Its market share in 2013 was just 1%. Where would you place these two products on the Boston matrix?**

Red Bull would be classed as a *star* since they have high market share in a high growth market. Full-throttle would sit in the *question mark* category. Like Red Bull, they are in a high growth market, however they currently hold a low share of the market.

4. **The windowless plane is predicted to be the future of aircraft. What is the main barrier that will hinder its growth?**

According to airspacemag.com, a long-haul plane will last 20 years or more. This means entry into the market will be slow and gradual, as existing aircraft fleets will take time to be withdrawn.

A secondary barrier may be how those who are nervous of flying perceive them.

CHAPTER 5

The peril of twin babies

My Aunt Kath called me excitedly the next day. She had spoken to someone who used to make bespoke bedding by hand and was happy to meet me. We drove around to her house the following evening.

The lady was called Brita and I would guess she was in her early sixties. When bringing up her children, she used her passion for sewing to make some extra cash for the family. Judging by the size of her house, she must have done pretty well because it was flippin' massive.

After introductions, we sat down in the living room with mugs of coffee.

"A good friend of mine called Sarah had asked me to make a personalised duvet set for her son's birthday. She knew I could sew and had seen some of the things I'd done around the house." Brita patted one of the cushions on the sofa, indicating they were hers. They were truly amazing cushions!

"He was such a sweet boy so I was happy to help. Since he loved football it was based on that. Anyway, it went down so well I thought, 'what about doing this for other people?' And that's how I started *Duvet Days.*"

"How did you promote the business?" I asked.

"Well, it started through word of mouth. I made it known to my friends what I was doing, and of course Sarah was singing my praises to everyone in her circle. But that only got me so far. I realised that to grow it, I'd need to take it nationwide. So I placed an advert in one of those ladies magazines and it really took off. This was before the days of websites and mobile phones. Everything was done by telephone and *snail mail*. Believe it or not, we did find ways to communicate before the days of computers!"

"How did you manage to personalise them so much? Didn't you just buy fabric on reels?" asked Aunt Kath.

"I would ask people to sketch out what kind of duvet they had in mind. You wouldn't believe some of the crazy stuff I got sent! We had a fantastic haberdashery in town at the time, so I would go down there and source fabric to match their desires. When it was impossible to find a good match, I would have to resort to some crochet, which added to the price. My husband was a good artist, so he would help turn their sketch into something more realistic and I would price it up based on the complexity and cost of the fabric needed."

"Wow!" I said, totally impressed by the way Brita had developed her business. "Did it take off?"

"It really did. But do you know why I think it did so well? My children always came first, so I was struggling to fulfil the orders I was being sent. So, there was a limit to how fast I could reasonably churn out the orders we were receiving. And this inadvertently created an extra demand for my products! Instead of putting people off, it meant my work was highly prized. I truly believe that if I'd employed lots of people to help me fulfil the orders, then it wouldn't have been half as successful, because there would have been no exclusivity."

I reflected on this and saw a connection. "It's a bit like when I go out with my friends into town on weekends. There is this nightclub that always has a massive queue outside. It always made us feel envious of the people inside. Then one time, we made it in. We had the most amazing time! I'm not sure it's any better than the other clubs, but the fact it's so hard to get in made it feel more special."

"Believe it or not, it was exactly the same for us when we were your age!" said Aunt Kath, smiling at Brita.

"Yes it was!" she replied. "If you think about a lot of the *über* successful brands today, they deliberately employ the same kind of approach. Exclusivity creates a greater sense of value in the product or service you receive. Some companies use this to charge more. We tried to remain fair and consistent. I suppose we could have doubled the fees once we had a surplus of orders, but I treated it as a hobby as much as a business, so we resisted the opportunity. I think that actually worked in our favour because it meant we got a lot of repeat business. And repeat business meant we didn't need to keep advertising all the time, so I suppose it actually saved us money."

"That's clever," I thought and said simultaneously.

"It wasn't intentional my dear, I can assure you. I just didn't believe in ripping people off. It's only now, when I look back, that I realise it probably made good business sense. After that first advert, I think we only ever advertised one more time in the fifteen years we were in business. Mind you, by making bespoke duvet covers, we were very much in a niche market. We had no desire to become a big player, as then we would lose our appeal. And do you know what I am most proud of with that business of mine?"

"You always made a profit?" I asked uncertainly.

"Goodness no!" replied Brita. "I don't take much satisfaction from the money side at all. In all of those years, I only had one customer who returned a cover asking for a refund! I must have made over two thousand duvet covers, yet had only one dissatisfied customer. I bet lots of businesses today would kill for that level of quality."

"That is impressive," I said.

Brita started to laugh. "Do you know why they returned it?" I shook my head. "The lady's daughter had just given birth to twin baby girls. She wanted two identical duvet covers in pink, with the names of her two granddaughters embroidered onto them. I made the first and it was lovely. The second was the last job I had to complete before we went off on a family holiday and I have to admit I rushed it. Of course, the lady noticed a couple of minor defects on the second one. If she hadn't received two, she might never have been aware. Anyway I took full responsibility, made her a perfect replacement and only charged her for one. You see, if you ensure that the operational side of your business is good, then the profit making will take care of itself. Assuming you price your products correctly, of course."

"My niece has developed a business idea of her own," said my Aunt. "As it's not far removed from what you did Brita, I'm sure she'd really value any advice you could give."

"Yes, I must admit your Aunt did hint at a superb idea you have hatched! But do tell me the details as I only know a little."

I proceeded to tell Brita all about my big idea.

"Well, I think that's a wonderful idea!" she said enthusiastically. "I don't know anyone that likes making beds and your idea sounds like a godsend." I was so relieved to hear someone be so positive after the lukewarm response I had received from Mum.

"Tell me," she continued, "have you thought about how you are going to make them?"

"Not as yet," I said. "My Uncle has advised me to figure out whether there is a market for it first."

"Well I'm a little old school, so I would have to disagree with your Uncle there." I saw her wink at Aunt Kath. "I believe in trusting your gut instinct. When I started my business, after completing that first gift for my friend, I had no idea whether I would get no more orders or a hundred. I didn't have all the information you youngsters have at your fingertips today, so I just took a chance! The important thing was we weren't risking our life savings on it. We already had the sewing equipment, so the only up front cost was the price of the advert, which I think was about £100."

"You don't think I should worry if there's a market for it, then?"

"Put it this way. Based on what you have told me, providing the material is of good quality and it doesn't look hideous, I would buy one."

"Me too," added Aunt Kath.

"So there, you have a 100% response rate so far. Granted we might be a little bit biased, but the idea is clearly good. If you had come up with some silly idea, then I'd tell you straight. I realise this is not what these business consultants would advise you, but I'm afraid the world of business is as simple as it always has been. If a product is of good quality, if it's fairly priced and if it satisfies a need, then you will always find customers."

"So how should I go about making them?" I asked awkwardly.

"Now that is indeed the question. I am guessing you are like me and don't want to throw all your hard earned savings at this?" she joked. "Well then, my advice would be to start a little cottage industry of your own, just as I did."

I'd heard that saying but never really given any thought to what it meant. "What is a cottage industry?"

"A cottage industry is how it used to work back in the day before the industrial revolution. People would make things in their own home and then traders would come along, buy their product from them and take them off to market. The traders would end up making more money of course, but the people in their cottages were able to live independently. And they were doubtless much better off than when the industrial revolution came along and people had to work for peanuts."

"But I can't sew," I said.

"You don't need to, my dear," responded Brita. "There are people out there like myself who can sew. You need to get in touch with them and agree to send business their way. You will find there are a number of people who will be more than willing to work with you."

"Who would source the materials?" asked Aunt Kath.

"Sadly, the haberdashery I used to buy from no longer exists. But I'm sure the seamstress you choose to work with will have her own sources. The key will be to find one who will supply small quantities, so you don't tie all your cash up in stock."

"How much do you think it will cost to make a duvet cover?"

"Now there's a question! Do you know why duvet covers make such great products to produce?"

I thought, but nothing sprung to mind. "Not really."

"Come on, think about it! What shape are they?"

"Rectangular?"

"Of course. Which means that not only are they really easy to cut, but there is very little wastage. Which is precisely what I realised all those years ago. Minimising waste and maximising efficiency are two key principles of business. Of course, I had to go and complicate things by letting the customer design their own, but as you are much smarter than me, you won't fall into this trap, will you?"

"Definitely not," I said.

"So, in answer to your question, a standard double duvet, plus pillows, requires somewhere in the region of 10m² of fabric. The quality of fabric you are going to need will cost in the region of £2 per square metre. Add on an additional couple of quid for your accessories, like buttons and yarn. A good machinist should be able to knock one up in around thirty minutes and charge around £15 per hour. So in total, I would say you're looking at about £30."

"That sounds a lot if I have to buy loads up front?" I asked.

"Let's not worry about that just yet. That's actually a lovely problem to have. The most important lesson I can teach you about business is to understand your margins."

"How do you mean?" I asked quizzically.

"Well, say it costs £30 to make a duvet. And say you charge £50, so you make £20 clear profit. That might sound good, and it is, if you sell 10,000 per year. But if you only sell 100, then it's not going to be enough at all. So you need to figure out what is a fair price for you and the customer, because once you fix a price, it becomes very difficult to change it."

"That sounds complicated."

"It isn't really, but you do need to get it right from day one, otherwise you are going to fail. Luckily, you can base your pricing on what is fair in the market."

"Do I need to decide all of this now?"

"Absolutely not, but it is something you need to be thinking of. I expect lots of businesses have messed up because of bad pricing. I do know someone who is local and might want to work with you, so I can hook you both up if you like?"

"Yes that would be great, thanks! But perhaps I need to do a little more research first?"

"Of course, my dear. You must take all the time you need."

"You've been really helpful, Brita," said Aunt Kath.

We stayed and talked a little longer, but it was now very clear that I needed to really understand this business before I got deeper into it.

What you've covered:

Theme	Amplification
Marketing	Compare niche marketing versus mass marketing
Operations	What is meant by 'operations management'?
Operations	The key stages of operations
Operations	The meaning of 'quality'
Financial	Why 'margins' are so important in business

Memory hook: The peril of twin babies

Think of Brita's returned pink duvet cover for a twin baby as an illustration of quality. The customer expected both duvets to be of identical quality. In business, quality is about 'consistency'.

So, key points to remember:

1. **Niche products/services** focus on a specific segment of the market - for Brita this was bespoke duvet covers. **Mass-market products/services** aim to meet the needs of most people in the marketplace – such as traditional duvet covers.
2. **Operations management** is the task of transforming inputs into outputs. So in Lucinda's case, fabric into a duvet cover.
3. The key **stages of operations** are: Raw materials, Manufacturing, Transportation, Retail and Recycling.
4. **Quality of operations** means producing products or offering services to a consistent level. So a customer expects the sandwich they receive in a cafe today to be of the same standard as the one they received yesterday. This includes how it tastes, the amount of filling, the way it's presented, the time it takes to make, etc. It is not to be confused with producing 'expensive' or 'luxury' items. Low priced products/services still need to maintain a good level of quality.
5. The **margin** is the difference between the selling price and the total cost of making the product/service. In most cases, it must be greater than zero and also large enough to cover the additional costs that are not incurred in production, such as marketing etc.

Now ask yourself:

1. Choco Noir Ltd. only sells handcrafted dark chocolates. They are very expensive to buy and contain high-end ingredients. What are the advantages and disadvantages of a niche product like this?
2. What is the key difference between a product and a service?
3. What would you consider to be the key operational objectives for a distribution company such as FedEx or Royal Mail when delivering a parcel?
4. Can you think of situations where a company would be prepared to sell a product for less than the cost of making it?

Now ask yourself (suggested answers):

1. **Choco Noir Ltd. only sells handcrafted dark chocolates. They are very expensive to buy and contain high-end ingredients. What are the advantages and disadvantages of a niche product like this?**

   Advantages:
   - **Loyalty**. Whilst they only appeal to a small section of the population, those they do sell to are more likely to remain loyal.
   - **Low threat**. They are less of a threat to bigger companies who are too busy competing with each other.
   - **Reduced marketing costs.** Their marketing costs are likely to be lower since they are not trying to appeal to everyone.
   - **Focus**. A focus on one specific product or service typically makes it easier to achieve high levels of quality and customer satisfaction.

   Disadvantages:
   - **Sensitivity**. They are more sensitive to small changes in the market – losing a few key customers could be very damaging.
   - **Economies of scale**. They lack the buying power and economies of scale enjoyed by larger businesses.
   - **Future threat**. If the market grows then they face the threat of bigger businesses moving in.
   - **Fragility**. If their product loses popularity, they have no fall back option, i.e. they have 'put all their eggs in one basket'.

2. **What is the key difference between a product and a service?**

   Unlike products, services are intangible. In other words, there is nothing physical to sell, so the customer can't see or feel it. This inevitably requires a different approach for marketing, since services need to be sold on perceived benefits and promises, more so than products.

3. **What would you consider to be the key operational objectives for a distribution company such as FedEx or Royal Mail when delivering a parcel?**

Customers expect a number of things when they receive a parcel. Firstly, they will expect it to arrive on time. Therefore, the logistics of moving parcels around the world in a timely fashion is key. In the case of fragile parcels, customers expect it to arrive in good physical condition. Consequently, safe handling of parcels is very important. Thirdly, in the case of multiple items, they will expect to receive the full shipment – lost in transit will not be received well.

From the company perspective, they will want the parcel to be delivered at a profit. So they will need their shipments to move around the world in an efficient manner.

4. **Can you think of situations where a company would be prepared to sell a product for less than the cost of making it?**

- **Shelf life**: Some products will have a shelf life and if the product is not sold as it reaches that shelf life, it becomes worthless. Most grocery stores heavily discount products in the final hours of shelf life to recoup some value, often at a loss.
- **Storage costs**: The task of storing products costs money, so companies will often sell a product at below its value to eliminate the cost of storage.
- **Cash flow**: Sometimes businesses need to sell old products to generate cash to buy new ones.
- **Fashion**: Some products, such as clothing, can quickly go out of fashion. Companies such as TK Maxx buy and sell out of season stock.

CHAPTER 6

The cloud of redundancy

The following evening was very productive in terms of my research. I'd learnt a little more about the type of fabric needed for bedding, specifically the fact that good quality bedding is mainly cotton and it needs to be a certain weight. I'd also looked a little wider at the breadth of online retailers of duvet covers, noting the general price-points across their range.

So when Mum called us for dinner and demanded a night at the table, as opposed to dinner in the front of the TV, my mind was buzzing with information. My brother ate in silence, so I told Mum all about my new discoveries.

She seemed a little distracted, but I continued talking anyway as I was excited about the fact nothing had really impressed me. Then it happened.

"Enough!" My brother missed his mouth with his fork of food, due to my Mum's bellow. "Lucinda, can we just have a peaceful family meal where I don't have to listen to your hair-brained scheme that is only going to cost us money we almost certainly don't have?"

As Bolognese sauce dripped from my brother's chin, Mum swiftly left the table and returned to the kitchen. I glared in mild disgust at my brother's carelessness, to which he shrugged his shoulders. I threw him a napkin, which only compounded the misery by landing on his plate. After a minute or so of waiting for a return that never came, I followed her into the kitchen. I found her sobbing next to the kettle.

"Mum, what's the matter?" I asked, putting my arm around her shoulder.

"I'm sorry, Lu," she sobbed. "I've just had a bad day at work, that's all. It was wrong of me to take it out on you."

"That's alright, I shouldn't have kept going on. What's happened?"

"Nothing you need to concern yourself about."

"Is it that woman again who's been hassling you about that stupid report?"

"Oh, I wish it was darling! Just ignore me."

"Come on, Mum, you've always told me not to hold onto stuff. A problem shared and all that."

"Oh, it's just more of the public sector nonsense. There might be some job cuts. I'm sure it will blow over."

My Mum worked for the local council and was responsible for housing management. She had hoped that the cuts wouldn't reach them. Now it seemed they had.

"It must be worse than that to make you sad, Mum. You're the most resilient person I know."

"That's nice of you to say, Lu." She poured some water from the kettle into her cup. "They announced some more cuts today. Re-structuring they call it. And it looks like it's going to affect my area, that's all. We need to save more money and now the cuts have hit us."

"And is that likely to include you?" I asked.

"They haven't specified how many jobs will go yet, but there are nine of us in the team and based on the figures they are talking about needing to save, I reckon that means around three to four of us facing redundancy."

"But how will the work get done with half of the staff gone?"

"They will ship what they can out to the private sector, I guess. They are already reducing their stock of council houses by selling them off."

"But they haven't said your job will go?"

"No, not yet. They are going to share their plans through individual consultation. It doesn't look good though. They've provided us with some labour productivity figures that claim we are costing almost twice as much to employ, compared to the value of our outputs. It's a stupid measure though. They are treating us like we are workers on a factory production line, churning out widgets. But our job is to support some of the most disadvantaged people in the community. I just don't know how we'll cope if I lose my job!" Mum started to cry again.

"It won't come to that Mum, you're brilliant at your job. And even if it does happen, they'll surely find you work elsewhere."

"I wish it worked like that, my love. Re-structuring is about roles and if your role is deemed to be non-essential in the new structure, then you will go. Then I would join what they call the redeployment pool, but there are so few jobs available in the public sector right now."

"So, what about the companies they are selling out to. Surely they will need people to manage their new housing?"

"Oh, there's no guarantee of that. They will probably want to maintain efficiencies so will just make the current people they employ do more."

"When will this happen?" I asked.

"Soon. The consultations will take place in the next few weeks and then they will announce the final structure. At least if my job goes, I will get some form of redundancy, due to my length of service. That will tide us over for a few months."

"Mum, I'm sure it won't come to that. They will just be doing it to weed out the people who do nothing."

"It's not that simple, I'm afraid Lu. Their main argument is that there are too many layers in the organisation. Apparently, we are quite *tall* which means there are too many people between the top and the bottom. They want to de-layer us to make a much *flatter* structure. Which means there will be less *chains of command*, which of course will save money. Unfortunately, as a team leader, that puts me right in the firing line."

"What exactly do you mean by 'chains of command'?"

"Well, it basically means the number of managers in the hierarchy. So I have five people who report to me. In HR speak, that's known as my *span of control*. If they remove me and have those five people report in to my boss Bridget, then they save money by removing a manager's salary. It's what they call *centralisation*, which pushes all the decision-making to the top of the organisation."

"But what if they decide to get rid of Bridget and keep you?"

"Well, judging by the organisational structure they sent out today, that's not going to happen. Mine and three other roles have been provisionally removed from the structure. So Bridget will have to manage lots more people."

"But she's not going to cope. And anyway, you're always saying how she doesn't understand your area. So it would never work."

"But that's not all. They're going to introduce *job share* and reduce the five to three. So there will be less people for Bridget to manage and she will delegate more of the authority to the three that remain."

"That's crazy though. You're always saying how overworked most of you are."

"I know love, but the council don't see it like that. You see, since they sold off lots of the council houses to private companies to create social housing, we have less property stock to manage. What they don't see is we have to do far more with them because they lumped *property maintenance* in with *regulation and energy management.*"

"Try not to worry, Mum. I'm sure it will work out fine in the end."

"Yes, maybe you will make your millions with this duvet thing and you can employ me!" She laughed.

"Mmm, I have a strict recruitment policy, you know!" She laughed even more. "Come on, let's go and finish eating. I promise not to mention duvets again."

We returned to the dining room. I could now see more clearly the scariness of adult life. Perhaps my business idea was just a stupid daydream? Maybe I should just finish college and get a job so I could help Mum to pay the bills.

What you've covered:

Theme	Amplification
Enterprise	The roles of the private and public sector
Human Resources	Redundancy and redeployment
Human Resources	Labour productivity as a measure of effectiveness
Organisational Design	The difference between flat and tall structures
Organisational Design	The meaning of delayering and reducing chains of command
Human Resources	Outsourcing of staff

Memory hook: The cloud of redundancy

Lucinda's Mum becomes emotional due to the threat of redundancy. One of the many functions of the Human Resource (HR) department is to manage employees when their jobs become at risk.

So, key points to remember:

1. The **public sector** is owned and principally funded by national or local government. It has three elements: **Public corporations** which sell products/services to the public; **Public services** such as the National Health Service; **Municipal services** which operate on a local basis such as sport centres or public parks.
2. An employee is made **redundant** when there is no longer a need for their job within the organisation.
3. **Redeployment** is the term for finding an employee alternative employment within the organisation as an alternative to making them redundant.
4. Some organisations decide to **outsource** an operation to another organisation. This means they pay another company to do that work on their behalf. Those people who currently work in that function could face redundancy or redeployment.

Now ask yourself:

1. Can you name some well-known public corporations in the UK?
2. Where does the public sector get its money?
3. Redundancy is one way in which a person can lose their job. Can you think of others?
4. What is the political reason why many people in the public sector have faced redundancy in recent years?
5. Can you think of common functions within organisations that face the risk of being outsourced?
6. What are the advantages and disadvantages of outsourcing for the organisation?

Now ask yourself (suggested answers):

1. **Can you name some well-known public corporations in the UK?**

   The National Health Service (NHS), the British Broadcasting Corporation (BBC) and the Post Office are all public corporations. When the government bought some of our banks during the financial crisis, they technically became public corporations for that period.

2. **Where does the public sector get its money?**

   a. **Tax.** Most public sector funding comes from taxes, such as Income Tax, VAT and Corporation Tax.
   b. **Investment.** The government also receives money by accepting investment from private individuals (through Treasury Bonds and Premium Bonds, for example), but also from investment banks. During uncertain economic times, investing in the public sector is seen as a safe haven.
   c. **Revenue** from public corporations also funds the public sector, e.g. the TV licensing fee.

3. **Redundancy is one way in which a person can lose their job. Can you think of others?**

   People can be dismissed (i.e. sacked) from their job if they underperform or act improperly (gross misconduct). Also, people can be redeployed if their job is no longer required. This means they continue working within the company but perform a different function.

4. **What is the political reason why many people in the public sector have faced redundancy in recent years?**

   The financial crisis, which began around 2008, caused some people within the public sector to lose their jobs or be redeployed. The government decided they needed to save money to reduce the nation's debt. This is known as austerity and has meant streamlining public services. Since the public sector does not generate revenue, the main options were to either reduce jobs or increase taxes.

5. **Can you think of common functions within organisations that face the risk of being outsourced?**

Service departments, such as *Human Resources* and *Finance*, often get outsourced. Another function that has commonly been outsourced over recent years is *Customer Services*. Many organisations have elected to outsource this to companies overseas in countries like India, where wages are lower.

6. **What are the advantages and disadvantages of outsourcing for the organisation?**

Advantages:
- **Money saving**. The company no longer has to pay the wages of employees. However, in addition to wages, a company also saves on paying National Insurance contributions and pension contributions, which can often be where savings are made.
- **Transfer of expertise**. If the outside supplier has specialist skills, then the company benefits from their expertise.
- **Lower headcount**. The company is deemed to be smaller (since those people are no longer counted as employers) and this can result in saving other costs, such as heating and IT. Being smaller in size can have additional benefits, such as public funding etc.

Disadvantages:
- **Quality control**. The company has lost an element of control over the quality of work provided.
- **Added cost**. If the company has to pay a premium for using outsourced staff, then it could be worse off than if it continued doing it in-house.
- **Loyalty/knowledge**. The external people recruited to do the work are not members of company staff. This could mean a reduction in loyalty or company knowledge, which may result in poor performance.

The next day, I went around to see Aunt Kath after college, as I often do. I told her all about my Mum's problems.

"I went through a similar thing myself when you were younger," she said.

"I didn't know that."

"You were only small, so we didn't bring it up in front of you. It was quite a big deal because Steve's consultancy business was in its early stages, so my regular wage provided a bit of added security."

"What job did you have?"

"I worked for a local law firm as a legal secretary. One of the partners to the firm did something majorly wrong and it affected business badly. We lost loads of clients and eventually they dissolved the partnership."

"Gosh, that must have been really bad?" I asked.

"Well, it was bad at the time because we all got tainted. I found it really hard to find other work, so I ended up becoming Company Secretary for

Steve. It just goes to show, no matter what type of business you work in, there is always a risk."

"I know. With Mum driving a VW, she keeps talking about all this emission stuff and how it will affect the sell-on value of her car."

"That was a big part of being a Company Secretary. I helped keep on top of all the administration. Things like filing the annual return to Companies House, dealing with all of the VAT returns and managing telephone calls. But there's also quite a lot of legislation to keep on top of. If you mess up on your obligations as a business, it can get you in a lot of trouble. VW are a high profile example of a company that didn't meet its commitment to environmental measures, but small businesses need to be vigilant too."

"Do you think Mum will be OK?"

"It's tough being in the public sector at the moment because of all this austerity. The challenge for the public sector is it doesn't add value to the country's economy. So in times of a downturn, it's always susceptible to cost cutting. This means they try to either make services more efficient by reducing jobs or merging departments. Or they will try to pass a lot of the work off to the third sector."

"What exactly is the third sector?"

"Good question. Some people call it the not-for-profit sector, which I'm pretty sure is the same thing. So it includes things like charities, social enterprises and mutual businesses. Do you remember me joking I was going to work for that company in the local news called 'Silver Surfers'?"

"The one that employed older people to do computer work at home?"

"That's the one. Well, that's an example of a social enterprise. They basically help people in the community who are of a certain age that can't find a job, but still need to work if their pension pot isn't enough to live on."

"So, social enterprises help certain groups of people who are disadvantaged?"

"Yes. Silver Surfers has been created because people are living longer, but not all can afford to retire completely. I think this problem is going to get worse if the medical advances they talk about materialise. It will mean the demographics change so the population contains lots more old fogies like me."

"You're not old!" I exclaimed.

"I certainly feel it sometimes. But it is a huge problem, just as it's a problem for young people finding work too. So, the apprenticeship programme Jamie Oliver started is another example of a social enterprise. *Fifteen*, I think it's called."

"But shouldn't the public sector be helping with society's problems?"

"Many people say it should, yes. So a change of government could lead to higher taxes to help pay for more support services. But the more you tax people, the less they have available to spend. Some of the work that social enterprises do overlaps with the public sector. So it can be a good solution to let some of the work go out, if it prevents tax hikes. Although that doesn't help your Mum because a lot of the old council houses that were public sector owned are now being sold off to social housing firms."

"If the third sector doesn't make any profit, what's the attraction of it, then?"

"Well they can, except it's not called profit in the third sector, it's known as surplus. But they must re-invest any surplus they make back into the enterprise, whereas private companies can distribute their profits to their shareholders through dividends."

"So, if I get my company going, will I be in the private sector?"

"I expect you would. You might start off as a *sole trader*, which means you would be responsible for the business. Or you could do what Steve and I did which is to create a *limited company*. If you decided to go into business with someone else, like the legal firm I used to work for, then that would be a *limited partnership*."

"Why would I choose to be a limited company over a sole trader?"

"If you set up as a limited company, then you basically work for the company, as well as being a shareholder. You would become a Company Director and the company would pay you a salary, which you could set yourself. Then at the end of the year, you might pay yourself a dividend as a shareholder, providing you have made a profit. But the main reason for setting up as a limited company is it limits your liability. So in other words, if something goes badly wrong, then the company is responsible, rather than you."

"But if I set up the company, doesn't that make me responsible?"

"It can do, if you have been seen to be acting irresponsibly as a Director. But if it was just bad luck then no, it is the company that takes the responsibility. If the company gets wound-up of course, meaning it is forced to cease trading, then all of the other people the company owes money to, known as its creditors, get paid off first. So if you invested money into the company, then you wouldn't get it paid back if the business failed."

"Maybe I should set-up as a social enterprise and employ disadvantaged people to help me? Then I would be benefitting the community."

"You could, but you would have a responsibility to those people who might become dependent on the work. At least if you contract businesses to make your products, they will have other customers too. So it would be less pressure on you to make it work."

"That's a good point. I'd hate to let all those people down."

"That's fine, Lu. I don't think you need to decide now, but I'm not sure if a social enterprise is the right way to go."

"Well, I feel like I've just interviewed you! You've taught me a lot though."

"I know, I feel like a University Lecturer! Ooh, speaking of which, I have someone I need to introduce you to. My friend Sandra has got a son who is doing a PhD at the university. He is studying people who are budding entrepreneurs and wants to follow and observe them as they grow their businesses. We both thought you might be ideal!"

"Blimey, that sounds a bit scary! I'm not sure."

"Well, I think you should go and meet him anyway. He's studied business, so he'll probably be much better informed than me and your Uncle."

"OK, well if you think I'll survive being around clever people, I'll give it a go. When do you want me to meet him?"

"Anytime you like. Can I give my friend Sandra your email address so he can contact you?"

I nodded.

"Great. By all accounts, he's a bit of a hunky devil!"

"Aunt Kath!" I said, slightly shocked at her choice of words for someone my age.

We carried on chatting about more girly stuff and then I walked home, hoping to find that Mum had some better news from work. Occasionally, my mind drifted to whether my Aunt's idea of a 'hunky devil' bore any resemblance to someone I would consider 'fit'. Her lifelong crush was on Richard Gere, so I didn't hold out much hope...

What you've covered:

Theme	Amplification
Enterprise	The role of the not-for-profit (third) sector
Enterprise	Sole trader versus a private limited company
Enterprise	The impact and implications of the legal structure of a business
Social factor in PEST	How the demographics of a population can affect business and peoples' lives
Environmental factors	The obligation of businesses to show responsibility to the environment

Memory hook: Silver Surfers

Silver Surfers is a social enterprise and therefore belongs to the not-for-profit sector. Its aim is to support socially disadvantaged people within its community.

So, key points to remember:

1. The not-for-profit sector can make profit - however it is called a surplus and it must be invested back into the enterprise.
2. A sole trader is a business that is owned and managed by one person. They have unlimited liability, which means they are responsible for any financial problems the business faces.
3. An enterprise can be incorporated as a company by registering it with Companies House. It has its own legal identity. The owners of the company therefore become shareholders (as well as employees) and are not personally responsible for its debts if the business fails.
4. All businesses must adhere to the Environmental Act in the country they operate in. This means if they are shown to pollute or cause some other environmental damage, then they could be prosecuted.

Now ask yourself:

1. Private limited companies end in 'Ltd'. Public limited companies end in 'plc'. Why are they called that and can you think of some examples?
2. What are the implications of a change in demographics to the world of business?
3. How do people who invest in companies through the stock market make money?
4. Has the focus on environmental concerns damaged or helped the business world?

Now ask yourself (suggested answers):

1. **Private limited companies end in 'Ltd'. Public limited companies end in 'plc'. Why are they called that and can you think of some examples?**

    A private limited company has control over who its shareholders are (hence 'private'). A plc company has opened up its shares to other companies and individuals. They will have done this to raise capital. However, they risk having the majority of their shares being bought out by a rival, which could force a takeover.

    The UKs leading plc's are listed on the FTSE100 index. Currently, plc's with the greatest market capitalisation on the index include Royal Dutch Shell, HSBC, Vodafone and BT.

    Some of the better-known private limited companies are John Lewis, Virgin, Arcadia and JCB.

2. **What are the implications of a change in demographics to the world of business?**

    The key demographic trends in the UK at present are migration and increasing life expectancy. With more people domiciled in the country and people being expected to live longer, increased pressure is placed on public services and the provision of food and clothing. However, these issues also affect the nature of products being demanded. Older people may require more healthcare products, for example.

    With more migrant workers in the UK needing jobs, some employers have taken advantage of this by recruiting them as lower paid workers. Moving forward, the pressure of an ageing population makes a rise in the retirement age more likely. This is then likely to create added responsibility on companies to find work for more people.

3. **How do people who invest in companies through the stock
    market make money?**

    Typically through two sources. Firstly, a shareholder will make a
    profit if he/she sells their shares at a higher price than they originally
    bought them for. In addition, if an attempt is made to take over the
    company, then existing shareholders may receive an offer to sell their
    shares at an inflated price.

    Secondly, if the company performs well, they will generally issue
    shareholders with a dividend (usually on an annual basis). This is
    effectively a share of the profits.

4. **Has the focus on environmental concerns damaged or helped
    the business world?**

    In some ways it adversely affects business. For example, many laws
    have been passed which serve to penalise companies who are
    deemed to be environmentally negligent. Also, some industries such
    as fishing and agriculture have quotas imposed on them to limit their
    trade.

    On the other hand, the rise in environmental concerns has created
    opportunities for new types of businesses. *Waste management* and
    renewable energy are good examples.

CHAPTER 8

Crazy Daisy

There were no major developments with my Mum. Apparently, she'd received a letter formerly inviting her to the 'consultation process'. She'd also made an appointment to see her Union Rep.

"What's the purpose of a union?" I asked innocently.

"They're kind of there to support me as an employee, in the event that I have a dispute with my employer. And potentially being made redundant is one of those disputes."

"Have you ever needed them before?"

"Urm, I can't say I have darling, no. Do you remember when I told you my friend Sally had been in trouble at work and got suspended?"

"Was that when she was accused of stealing, but you all knew she would never steal anything from anybody?"

"That was it, yes. Well, the trade union more or less acted as her lawyers and helped her win the case. It was the craziest thing ever because the woman that accused her of stealing, who was called Daisy, was the one that did it all along and was covering her own back. Crazy Daisy we called her. She was a nasty piece of work! Poor Sally was never the same after that and jumped ship at the first opportunity."

"Crazy Daisy! That's hilarious. Do you have nicknames for all your workmates?"

My Mum poured herself a glass of white wine and offered me one. I'd started drinking with my friends, but it just felt a bit weird drinking with my Mum, even if I was of legal age, so I said no.

"So technically, could I go to the teenager union and get them to stop you encouraging me to be a teenage alcoholic?" I said jokingly.

"Yes, if you can find a union that supports goody-two-shoes teenagers! Another thing unions do is challenge employers who try to enforce unfair regulations and campaign for improved working conditions. So if you find this teenager union of yours, you can see if they are willing to push for less chores in return for more spending money."

"I might just Google it later."

"Where would you kids be without Google, eh?"

"Like you never use it, Mum? You're on it all the time!"

"Yeah, I might just start searching for a new job later. I might well be needing one."

I decided to change the conversation, hoping it would distract her. "Aunt Kath has put me in touch with this guy she knows through someone called Sandra. He works at the university and wants to talk to me about my business idea."

"Are you going to see him?"

"I promised I would, although it sounds a bit scary to me."

"Oh, I'm sure it will be fine. I'll come with you, if you like?"

"It's OK Mum, I'm a big girl now. I'm just worried he's going to ask me loads of really clever questions that I won't know the answers to and make me feel stupid."

"You're a bright girl my love, so don't you worry. I'm sure it will be just fine. Where are you meeting him and when, just so I know?"

"I'm pretty sure he's not a serial killer, Mum! We've not planned anything yet. He's going to email me I think. But it will be somewhere around the university, I guess."

"OK, well still let me know when you've made the arrangements, even if he isn't a serial killer! How is your idea coming on?"

"It's pretty good. I've done a lot of research now, so I know way more about duvet covers than any normal eighteen year old should."

"So what are you planning?"

"I'm thinking maybe to set up a limited company, buying small quantities of stock and then selling online."

"Where will you get them made?"

"Aunt Kath's friend Brita knows people locally who might be willing to work with me. So I could maybe go down that route."

"Is it going to cost a lot to set-up? You have some savings and I have a little put away, but if it is going to run into thousands, then we might really struggle."

"I haven't really looked into the finances yet. Uncle Steve thinks I should research the market first and worry about that later. He says if the idea is good enough, we will find a way to make it work. I just worry that all this research I'm doing is not intelligent enough for when I go meet this guy from the university."

"Nonsense! What you've said makes total sense. Anyway, don't worry about what you don't know, just tell him all that you've told me. Besides, if he's the expert, he should be able to help you."

"We'll see."

"Right, dinner is ready. Can you go and call your brother please."

What you've covered:

Theme	Amplification
Employer/employee relationships	The role of trade unions

Memory hook: Crazy Daisy

Use the story of Crazy Daisy to recall how one role of trade unions is to support workers in the event of disputes. This includes representing them should they be accused of doing something wrong.

So, key point to remember:

A trade union is an organisation whose members are workers of a particular industry or set of industries. Their role is to support its workers rights by campaigning and negotiating with the employers on the workers' behalf.

Now ask yourself:

1. What other types of decisions would trade unions be involved with?

Now ask yourself (suggested answers):

1. **What other types of decisions would trade unions be involved with?**

    Trade Unions will get involved in any decisions that affect the rights and treatment of their workers. This will often involve campaigning for and negotiating improved legislation, such as maternity/paternity leave, time available for breaks, additional vacation leave etc. If workers are offered a pay rise, then they are likely to challenge the value of any rise that is deemed too low. Recently, the highly publicised campaign for junior doctor contracts involved significant trade union intervention.

CHAPTER 9

Extra-chunky tomato sauce

Dear Lucinda,

I was delighted to hear about your passion for business. I understand that you have an exciting idea for a new venture?

Please let me explain a little about myself. I graduated last year with a degree in Business Management and decided to continue studying, but this time for a PhD – glutton for punishment! My studies now are focused on one project, which is to better understand how people go from the idea stage to a fully operational enterprise. As part of this project, I want to work alongside people like you and chart their progress.

It is possible that you could be one of the people within my study, providing your project falls within certain criteria. However, if you do join the study, there is unfortunately a limit to how much I can actually help you. The reason for that is called bias. By giving advice, I might be seen to be influencing the outcomes of my study. Plus, we shouldn't assume my advice would necessarily be any good! ☺

Anyway, enough about me. I'd love to learn more about your idea. So if you'd like to talk freely about any of it, do please let me know what days and time suit you best!

Kind Regards,
Alex Chapman

I responded by saying I would be delighted to speak with him and set up a meeting after my college classes later that week.

In the meantime, I got really absorbed by some video links sent to me by Uncle Steve from a website called ted.com. There were loads of videos to choose, including ones by famous people like Steve Jobs and Bill Gates. I found myself learning lots of really interesting stuff that made me want to run my own business even more. I was beginning to feel like I had found my true self!

One particular link was to a presentation called 'What Makes Businesses Work' by a guy called Bill Gross. He identified five key factors that made successful companies such as YouTube, Instagram and AirBnB succeed, when similar ideas failed. They were:

1. The idea
2. Funding
3. The business model
4. The team
5. Timing.

He'd spent lots of time analysing hundreds of successful businesses and failures to help determine which factors were most important. When he revealed the five factors, I felt certain that the idea itself would be the most important factor. If the idea is a bad one, then surely any venture is doomed to failure?

To my surprise, his most important factor was the timing of when the business was created. He used an example of a company he had created in the area of online video. It was launched before broadband speeds had progressed and before the web was really ready for videos. It lost him millions of dollars and he closed it down. Yet just a couple of years later, when broadband had improved and Flash software was created, YouTube came along and has since grown into something huge. This was all down to timing.

I found it really useful to consider those five factors against my idea. I hadn't thought that the timing of it was in any way important, but now started to think about it. I guess the world had recently emerged from a major economic recession, which would have affected people's ability to spend money on non-essential stuff. I could imagine people having to 'make do' when times are hard and remember Uncle Steve telling me how Hyundai had offered customers who purchased their cars on hire purchase the opportunity to return it, if they lost their job and could no longer afford to make repayments. He said it was genius because people were buying more Hyundai cars during the recession due to the peace of mind of the offer. I guess returning used duvet covers was not an option, particularly if they came from my little brother's room!

It also occurred to me that I didn't really understand what he meant by a business model. I wondered if I should ask Alex what a business model is? Although, I didn't want to appear stupid if it's really obvious, so decided to ask Uncle Steve first! My team was a bit of an irrelevance, since it would only be me, and I hadn't even thought about funding yet.

Then I found another video on the website that totally changed my understanding of business! I suddenly realised that I had been thinking about this duvet cover idea all wrong. It was scary and exciting at the same time! The talk was by someone called Malcolm Gladwell and it was all about tomato sauce. In particular, how a man by the name of Howard Moskowitz changed the future of tomato sauce forever.

What I realised was that there is no such thing as the perfect tomato sauce, just as there is no such thing as the perfect cup of coffee. Or in my case, the perfect duvet cover. The harsh reality is that people like different kinds of tomato sauce. Now, as I write this, it seems pretty obvious. Not all of us prefer iPhones. In fact, Samsung sell more smartphones than Apple. But back in the 1980s, it wasn't obvious that people preferred different tomato sauce. Manufacturers were all desperately searching for the single, most perfect recipe for tomato sauce. And then, Howard Moskowitz discovered a particular group of consumers that none of the manufacturers knew existed. These people wanted their tomato sauce 'extra-chunky'.

It turns out that this is what is known as *market segmentation*. And it means that the goal of most businesses should be to sell to a particular segment, rather than attempt to sell to everyone. So, Brita was selling her handmade duvet covers to a small segment of people, which is why she referred to it as a niche market.

This got me thinking: which segment of people would I be selling my duvet covers to? Until that moment, I had naively assumed that everyone would want my duvet cover because it's clearly a better design. But not everyone might agree with me? Some annoyingly capable people might actually be very skilled at fitting duvets into covers. Others may be strange enough to actually enjoy the challenge. And I suppose some people may not even care less how their duvet cover fits, so long as it looks nice.

Which all presented me with a problem. I had no idea how to figure out to whom I should be selling. For example, won't older people find the traditional duvet cover approach particularly strenuous? But then, older people tend to be stuck in their ways and not liking change. Also, isn't a duvet considered quite a modern approach to bedding? I was thinking about my Grandma who still seems to use lots of sheets, instead of a duvet.

So perhaps I should target young people like me, who are not anchored to the traditional way? That would influence the choice of colours and patterns for the bedding. If I got it wrong by choosing more traditional designs aimed at older people, when in fact it is young people who would be most likely to buy, then I would not hit my sales targets.

And then what about gender? It's probably natural to assume that most people who buy duvet covers are women, so maybe the designs should be more feminine? But then you have also got men. They need to sleep too!

From searching on the web, I realised this was known as demographic segmentation. But there were other ways of doing it, such as by geography, income or behaviour. So, selling only to people in my own area would be one solution. But that would be very limiting and might need to be done through a shop. More expense!

Segmenting by income would either involve selling as cheaply as possible to attract low-income households, or selling at a high price to make them more exclusive. I guess if I charged too much, less people would be prepared to buy them. And people that spend loads of money on bedding probably don't buy them online. They would go to Selfridges or John Lewis or someplace like that. But then I don't want them to be really cheap and nasty either. So, middle of the range is probably the solution.

Behavioural segmentation did seem to be a part of my plan. After all, I was specifically targeting people who find the traditional approach irritating. But how do I identify these people? They don't walk down the street with a sign on their back saying 'I'm a moron who can't put a duvet cover on'. I decided this was a question for Uncle Steve. Or Alex?

What you've covered:

Theme	Amplification
Enterprise	Identifying business opportunities
Enterprise	The components of making a successful enterprise
Markets	The meaning of market segmentation and its importance to a business
Markets	The different ways in which a market can be segmented

Memory hook: Extra-chunky tomato sauce

Use Howard Moskowitz's discovery of extra-chunky tomato sauce lovers as a reference point for market segmentation. Think of the world as a cake - businesses need to cut a slice of the cake and only sell their product or service to that slice. That slice is the set of customers who are interested in their product/service. The rest of the cake is of no interest to them. That is segmentation.

So, key points to remember:

1. According to Bill Gross, having a good business idea is just one aspect of creating a good business. Other needs include: timing, having a good business model, acquiring funding and creating a strong team.
2. Market segmentation is about accepting that not everyone will want to buy your product or service and then developing the business around those people who are in your segment(s).
3. Markets can be segmented by: demographics, geography, income and behaviours.

Now ask yourself:

1. Which industries can you think of where timing is particularly important?
2. What are the advantages and disadvantages of having lots of different segments?
3. How might a manufacturer of umbrellas segment their market?
4. Are there any companies where market segmentation doesn't seem to be important?

Now ask yourself (suggested answers):

1. **Which industries can you think of where timing is particularly important?**

   Any product or service that is likely to have a short life cycle: fireworks ahead of Bonfire Night, for example, will require good timing. Also, seasonal sales opportunities such as Christmas, Valentine's Day and Easter will make timing highly relevant. Historically, timing the release of music singles or albums has been important.

2. **What are the advantages and disadvantages of having lots of different segments?**

   Advantages:
   - A broad range of different customers will be serviced.
   - The company will have a better understanding of successful segments and drop those that don't work.
   - The company can cross-sell products from one segment to another, i.e. segment B could be interested because they see segment A using their product/service. For example, travel websites sell holidays to a variety of different segments.

   Disadvantages:
   - Customers may be confused by the choices available to them.
   - The company may overstretch itself by trying to meet so many different markets. Perhaps multiple marketing campaigns will be required, which would be costly.
   - Some segments may reject a product or service if it's known they serve another segment. For example, young people may not be attracted to a product or service if it also appeals to their parents.
   - The level of physical stock required could be an issue.

3. **How might a manufacturer of umbrellas segment their market?**

- Sports such as golf fall into a segment requiring high performance.
- Gender preferences are likely to influence umbrella design, e.g. colour or size.
- Quality is a key differentiator for the market – ranging from high quality to budget (e.g. disposable umbrellas for sale at outdoor events).
- Innovative segments such as umbrellas that attach to the body rather than be hand held may also be considered.

4. **Are there any companies where market segmentation doesn't seem to be important?**

It is rare to find industries with no strong need to segment. Some do exist, however:

- Apple, Microsoft and Intel all have broad appeal across most segments.
- Price comparison websites typically appeal to a cross-section of demographics.
- Cinemas serve a wide variety of segments.

CHAPTER 10

Tesla

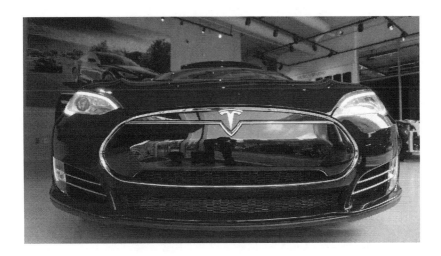

I felt incredibly nervous walking into the university to meet Alex. I'd only ever been there once before and that was with school. Everyone I walked past seemed really relaxed and were having a good time. I think most of my nerves were about meeting Alex.

I found his building and went over to reception. The person on the desk made a quick phone call and told me to take a seat as he'd be down in a couple of minutes. No turning back now!

The two minutes went really fast. Too fast. Alex came bounding down the stairs. He was tall, slim and well dressed. As he shook my hand, I noticed his piercing green eyes and smile. He seemed very friendly. And handsome!

"Come on up to my room – I've put the kettle on!" he said, ushering me back up the stairs he'd just come down.

We soon arrived at his room. It was enormous. "Is this room all yours?" I asked in surprise.

"Ha, I wish! I share it with two other researchers."

Since there were three desks with three separate computers on them, I should have figured that out myself. I immediately felt silly. He made us both a cup of coffee and we sat together on the table in the middle of the room.

"So, what's university life like?" I asked, genuinely interested. I realised that I was tapping my fingers against the cup, which was always my sign of nerves. I told myself to stop and relax.

"It's great!" he replied enthusiastically. He didn't seem nervous at all. In fact, he seemed so confident that I couldn't imagine him ever getting nervous. "I get to do something I really love doing and I'm surrounded by interesting people."

"You really love studying for exams?"

"Ha! Well maybe not the exam bit! This PhD is all research, so I've said goodbye to exams for the time being."

"You must be really clever?" I asked, and then blushed for asking such a dumb question.

"Nah, not really. These two are much cleverer than I am," he said, pointing at the desks behind me. "Natasha, who sits there, is an expert in economics. I'm in awe of her all the time."

I felt a ridiculous pang of jealousy for some poor girl I'd never met! There was a momentary awkward pause. He seemed to be lost for a moment, staring at Natasha's desk. Perhaps she was his girlfriend?

"So, what are you an expert in?" I asked. Another stupid question as he'd already told me in his email.

"Well, my area is entrepreneurship. I love the idea that anyone can start their own business, irrespective of who they are and their personal circumstances. In a world of privilege and unfairness, I think it's a great leveller. Many of the multi-millionaire tycoons we see on TV came from fairly poor backgrounds."

"But don't they need money in the first place to set it up?" I asked.

"Yes they do, but your Richard Branson's and Alan Sugar's of the world built their businesses by learning to buy and sell at a young age. They accumulated wealth early through trading, so when they moved into something bigger, they had a track record that made them credible. The world has changed a lot now through technology. Take crowdfunding, for example. People can acquire investment for a business simply by persuading others to invest in it. There's a guy that has amassed seventy million dollars of funding, just to build a computer game. Imagine that! However the principle is still the same – he has had to prove to people that he's worthy of investment."

He paused for a slurp of coffee. I was absorbed by his passion and energy and felt I could listen to him talk all evening.

"How's the coffee?" he asked. "It's rubbish isn't it!"

"No, it's fine," I lied.

"Coffee is a fascinating product. Do you think we consume more coffee in the UK now than we did ten years ago?"

I'd never really thought about it, but now wished I'd given it a lot more consideration! He was asking me a question and I really should provide an intelligent answer. 'Think woman', I told myself inside, but all I could think about was his eyes looking deeply into mine.

"Well, I guess with all the coffee shops we have today, we must do," I blurted, relieved that something had come to mind.

"You would think so, wouldn't you? But in fact we don't, even though it's become a huge global industry."

"That doesn't make sense," I said, genuinely confused.

"I know, I agree with you. But the way we consume coffee now, compared to the way people consumed coffee when we were kids, has changed dramatically."

"Has it?" I asked, noticing gratefully that he had categorised us both as though we were the same age. Right now, I felt light years away from him in age.

"Definitely. A generation ago, coffee was consumed throughout the day and made mainly by us, using a kettle. Like this awful instant coffee I've given you! Consumers today tend to give it more status, like it's some kind of reward. It's still part of a daily routine, yet it's not consumed so often. So as a nation, we drink more or less the same volume of coffee as before, but the cost per cup has gone up way above inflation because it's moved from being a functional beverage to a social occasion or personal indulgence."

"Wow," I thought, and realised I had blurted it out whilst thinking it. Which made me blush again. "I'd never thought of it like that."

"I know right! We always think of market growth in terms of a new invention, products becoming more popular, or something becoming scarce. Yet sometimes, a market can grow simply because the way in which customers interact with the product changes. I think that's why I love studying business so much. The logic and thinking is quite deep and yet the evidence is all around us."

I thought about what he had just said in relation to my idea and it kind of made sense. I am trying to get people to change the way they interact with duvets, even though I know the demand for duvets is not going to increase. However, I didn't get long to think about it as we moved on to another example.

"You know, a company that really interests me right now is Tesla. Have you heard of them?" I shook my head. "OK, well Tesla make cars. Except, instead of making cars that run on petrol, they concentrate only on electric cars."

"So it must be really hard for them to sell any then?" I asked.

"You'd think so, wouldn't you? In fact, they're doing really well. Tesla has been going for about fifteen years, but has only actually been selling their cars in the last five or so. All their effort before that was in R&D."

"What's R&D?" I asked, feeling silly.

"Sorry, Research and Development. They basically took a huge gamble that electric vehicles were the future. Ever since we knew that oil was going to run out, companies have been speculating on what the future will be. So they spent years creating electric batteries that can power a car for as long as possible without needing charge. Theirs can go for up to three hundred miles, which is much better than any other electric car currently. So they are a great example of a company in a niche market that is set to become mass market in the future."

"Why would someone buy an electric car when everyone else buys normal cars?" I asked.

"That's a good question. You might think people do it because they feel passionate about the environment. But that argument doesn't really hold true because cars are not particularly good for the environment, whichever way they are fuelled. You will always get people who like to be different and Tesla is certainly that. However, I think most people thought it would save money compared to the price of petrol. That was before the price of oil came tumbling down though. The car industry uses market research a lot. It turns out that people consider electric to be an acceptable option to petrol when the distance they can go without stopping to refuel is two hundred miles or more. Below that and people feel the hassle of running out of charge outweighs the financial benefits. By getting their batteries to run for three hundred miles, Tesla make themselves the clear market leader."

He paused for another slurp. "The reason why I find them most fascinating is that on the surface they appear to go against good business sense. For example, gambling on one innovation, when we could just have easily abandoned electric in favour of rapeseed oil or something. Yet in fact, they totally get it. Their cars are built to a really high spec and fall into the luxury car bracket. Which you might think is madness when they need to recoup their investment, because hardly anyone can afford to buy one. But it makes total sense because they realise that their main appeal is to early adopters – the people who like to get in on technology before it becomes mainstream. And early adopters are always prepared to pay a premium. Yet those people, who are prepared to pay a premium for a car, expect a really good car. So they give them a really good car that virtually nobody else on the road is driving. And then next year, I think they plan to launch a new affordable model that will appeal to the masses because

Tesla is associated with luxury. It's genius! And they promote their product in a totally different way to their competitors."

"In what way?" I asked.

"Well, for starters, they have never placed an advert. Anywhere. All of their promotion is done through PR. They have no dealerships like other car companies. Instead, they have stores in retail high streets. So this means they really get noticed, because who would expect to find a car shop next to a bank? And they fit them out in a really trendy way so they look like Apple stores."

I was taking in what he was saying whilst marvelling at his passion. "I tell you what," he said, "I feel really bad for giving you rubbish coffee. Why don't we go down the road to a proper coffee shop and I'll buy you a good one. You can tell me all about your business idea and we can do it in the name of market research on the growth of the coffee market!"

What you've covered:

Theme	Amplification
Finance	The use of crowdfunding as a source of finance
Operations	The role of Research and Development (R&D)
Environment	The role of business in supporting environmental issues
Technology	The transition from early adopters to mainstream
Marketing	The role of public relations (PR) in promotion

Memory hook: Tesla

Tesla is a great example of a company that is trying to solve global problems (such as environmental impact) whilst becoming profitable. They also do things differently to most other companies, which helps to generate good PR.

So, key points to remember:

1. *Crowdfunding* is when lots of people invest in a business by making donations. Incentives are offered to induce people to donate, which usually involve giving them free or discounted products. Peer-to-peer lending is similar, except the sums provided are usually larger and the investors are likely to require a financial payback of their money, with interest.

2. *R&D* is the stage of business development that aims to drive innovation and test to see whether products are viable, before they are released for sale.

3. *Early adopters* are people who buy a product before the mainstream get involved. They play a crucial role in helping to decide whether a new innovation takes off.

4. *Public Relations* is a marketing activity that generates interest through news stories. It can include being featured on TV, radio, YouTube, newspapers and magazines. Unlike advertising, it doesn't typically cost anything.

Now ask yourself:

1. Have you ever been an early adopter of a product? If so, what were your reasons for buying it?
2. What kinds of sub-sectors exist within the environmental industry?
3. Sometimes companies face negative PR. Can you think of any particular examples of this?
4. Can you find any examples online of crowdfunding?

Now ask yourself (suggested answers):

1.   **Have you ever been an early adopter of a product? If so, what were your reasons for buying it?**

     Some early adopters are passionate about the technology or innovation aspect. Others like having trendy products before their friends do. Those for whom money is no object, will often buy something, simply because they can.

2.   **What kinds of sub-sectors exist within the environmental industry?**

     a.   Renewable energy installation, e.g. solar, biomass, wind turbines etc.
     b.   Environmental consultancy and assessment.
     c.   Waste management.
     d.   Conservation management, e.g. forestry, preservation of wildlife and horticulture etc.
     e.   Organic agriculture.
     f.   Air and water quality management.

3.   **Sometimes companies face negative PR. Can you think of any particular examples of this?**

     Car manufacturers often receive negative PR. Volkswagen endured very bad PR over their emissions failings. Recently, Tesla has faced adverse PR due to the death of a driver using their autopilot functionality. Tesco have been criticised for inaccurate financial reporting and dumping kids bicycles that could have been recycled. Marks & Spencer have received widespread negative PR in recent years for bad decision-making over their clothing ranges.

4.   **Can you find any examples online of crowd funding?**

     Two well-known websites are: www.crowfunder.co.uk and www.kickstarter.com. Try visiting them!

CHAPTER 11

Vanilla latte

We walked briskly to the local coffee shop, talking about music – it turned out we both had tickets to the same gig by the Vaccines in a couple of months time, and sat ourselves on some comfy sofas with frothing vanilla lattes. It seemed we had the same taste in coffee as well as music!

"So, as I mentioned in my email, my job is to study people like you who have great ideas. Your idea is particularly interesting because you will be in the tertiary sector. I don't have many businesses in that sector so it would be really good to have you on board."

"Why is it called the tertiary sector?"

"The primary sector is about extracting stuff. So mining coal or catching fish would be primary. The secondary sector turns those raw materials into a final product. The tertiary sector provides services to the public, such as retailing the product or delivering the coal."

"Oh right, but if I'm manufacturing them too, wouldn't that make me secondary?"

"If you were making them yourself then yes, but I guess you will be paying someone else to make them for you?"

"Yes, I definitely will!"

"That's good. Otherwise, you'll be too busy to meet me for my research! So with your consent, I will then monitor and record your progress over the first year."

"Not with a video camera, I hope?" I asked.

"I wish!" He seemed to blush at this. "No, just to keep interviewing you and finding out all of the things you experience. I'll be doing it with others too!" he added, seeming slightly embarrassed.

"So, I won't have you all to myself? That's a pity." I was growing in confidence away from his room.

"Well, obviously I might have some favourite subjects!"

"Subjects? What, so I'll be one of your subjects, will I?"

"Oh man, bad choice of words! Obviously, it's an experiment, and experiments consist of subjects. But you'll be so much more than just a rat in a cage."

"A rat in a cage? Alex, you're so digging a hole here - I'd quit while you're behind! I hope you don't recruit all your subjects like this?"

It felt really nice to be flirting with him in this way. The last time I experienced anything similar was at a drunken night out with college friends over Christmas and that got really awkward. This felt so much more natural – and exciting at the same time!

"So, what are you hoping to get out of spying on me in my cage for the next year?" I asked.

He seemed to click back into professional mode, so I sensed the flirting was over, or on hold for a while. "Lots of things. I need to understand how entrepreneurs think and whether their actions are consistent with those thought processes. Then I need to understand the barriers they face, both in terms of their own limitations and those imposed by others. Basically, us academics think we know how entrepreneurs become successful – or fail – but few people have actually studied it in this way."

"You know, I've not really progressed my idea much beyond thinking it up, so I'm not sure how useful I can be to you?"

"No, that's perfect!" he said eagerly. "I really need people as they start on their journey as one of the assumptions to my work is that those early stages are key to their chances of success."

"Will I have to be available in the daytime? Only I have college three days per week."

"Not at all. Entrepreneurs rarely work normal office hours, so I'm expecting that. I haven't got any commitments to worry about."

"No girlfriends giving you grief over who you are meeting in coffee shops at five o'clock in the afternoon?"

"If I did, they would soon become an ex!"

I wasn't sure what to read into that.

"So, tell me about your idea," he continued quickly. I told him all about the idea and how it came about.

"Now it's explained, I can easily see why your idea is a great improvement on traditional duvet covers!" he responded enthusiastically. "It fits really well with a current trend in consumerism towards making jobs easier and simpler."

"Does it?" I asked.

"Absolutely. Think about how little time people have today and how they crave time to themselves. One of the big domestic growth markets right now is the clothes ironing service. If people can free up a couple of hours of their week by not ironing, then many will pay for that opportunity. That then creates other business opportunities. So there's now a mobile app that enables you to find an ironing service in your area. In fact, that makes me think you should try to source fabric for your duvets that is easy iron. Then you can really pin your idea on this concept of re-claiming time back from daily life."

"That's really good to know."

"Technically, I'm not supposed to provide you with any advice or guidance during the study, but as you haven't signed up yet, it doesn't matter."

"Well, I might play hard to get a bit longer then and take more advantage of your good ideas!"

"Alright, but the first two ideas are free. After that, I might have to start charging!" he joked. At least, I assumed he was joking.

"So what do you think I should do next? Only my Uncle says I need to keep researching, but I feel like I've kind of exhausted that."

"I hope he's told you to write all of this research down? Only you will need it for your business plan."

"Yes I've been making notes, but I want to get started now."

"Technically, you are currently in the feasibility stage. So you need to be investigating whether this could actually work and whether there is a need for it, or not. So your research is an important part of that. Then you will need to move on to writing a business plan. If you are seeking funding from a bank or an investor, then you will need to follow a formal business plan structure. But the mistake many people starting out make is to assume the business plan is not for their own benefit too. If you think about it, practically every plan you make in life is for yourself. Why should a business plan be any different? Think of it as a road map showing you where you are going, why you want to go there, what you will be doing along the way and what it looks like when you arrive. And also, if you deviate from the route, it helps remind you what needs doing to get back on track."

"That's a lot of questions. Why do I want to explain why I am going there? Isn't it obvious?"

"Not for everyone, no. A lot of people start businesses for very different reasons other than making lots of money and buying a remote Caribbean island. So many social enterprises are set up to help improve the lives of others. Environmental enterprises are there to help us with sustainability and keeping the planet alive. Some people just set up an SME so they can have a more flexible lifestyle or to fit in around their children and stuff."

"Did you say SME? What's one of those?"

"Sorry, that's me using technical terms again! SME stands for 'small to medium enterprise'. If you think about the word 'enterprise', it kind of means what it says: 'how to be enterprising'. So business is all about finding solutions for things that people need now or in the future, and of course profiting from that. Although in the case of a social enterprise, you don't make a profit. Instead, it must be called a surplus. So underneath the umbrella of 'enterprise', you have lots of different companies. The really big ones that trade all around the world, we call multi-national corporations – or MNCs. Then you have large national ones, which is usually if they employ over 250 staff. Then, there are your SMEs. And finally, you have micro-businesses, which are often just one person or a small group of people."

"And everyone wants to grow into a large one, right? What did you call them – MNCs?"

"Not necessarily. The bigger the company gets, the more complicated it becomes and many people don't want that degree of complexity. Plus, for many people, that means a loss of control. It's easy to control your little business employing five people. When you have five thousand employees, it becomes a little harder. Plus, a lot of people say small businesses are more fun and less bureaucratic."

"But to be really secure and earn lots of money, companies have to grow into something big?"

"Most of the time, but not always. Lots of big companies still go bust. Take Woolworths or HMV, for example. And also, many small businesses can still earn lots of money, yet stay small. Tech companies can be worth billions whilst still only employing a handful of people. Most of them end up selling the idea on to a Google or an Amazon. I much prefer small businesses, they are more interesting."

"I guess so. But I still think it pays to be big."

"And it was going so well – the Vaccines, vanilla lattes! I definitely think it's more exciting to be a small enterprise. You can be agile, you can relate easier to the men and women in the street…"

"And you can go out of business and end up a pauper."

"Well yeah, but that's the risk isn't it. And isn't that why you want to start making duvet covers that people actually fall in love with, rather than the run-of-the-mill ones lining up on department store shelves?"

"Can anyone fall in love with a duvet cover?"

"They can fall in love under a duvet cover!"

I laughed. A proper belly laugh. "Ha! Maybe that should be my marketing slogan!"

"Yeah, the duvet cover that prevents divorce!"

We paused. And laughed some more, glancing at each other in a way that was somewhere between relaxed and awkward. Our coffee cups were empty.

"I suppose I should be heading back," I said.

"Would you like a lift home?" he asked.

"A gentleman too?! Thanks, but I've got my bike, so I'll be home in no time."

"Right. Well, are you on board with my study then? I promise to buy your first duvet cover. As long as it's not bubble-gum pink!"

"Make it two duvet covers and you've got a deal."

"Two and I'll get all my family and friends to buy one too."

"That's poor negotiation – I was sold on just your two."

"Yeah, but I was prepared to buy up to five."

"Damn! I so need to improve my sales skills!"

We laughed as we left the coffee shop. Then he reached for my hand and gave it a gentle kiss. I'd never been kissed on the hand before.

"Do you kiss all of your 'subjects' on the hand?"

"Just the pretty ones!"

And with that, we left. I smiled all the way to collecting my bike and most of the journey home.

What you've covered:

Theme	Amplification
Enterprise	What are meant by 'SME' and 'MNC'?
Enterprise	The difference between primary, secondary and tertiary sectors
Enterprise	The financial and non-financial motives of entrepreneurs
Enterprise	The impact of entrepreneurs and SMEs on businesses and the economy
Business plans	The reasons for writing a business plan

Memory hook: Vanilla latte

Lucinda and Alex drink vanilla lattes together in a small, independent coffee shop (an SME), which contrasts with Starbucks (an MNC).

Then recall the three elements that go into getting a product to market - growing the coffee beans (primary), turning them into packaged coffee (secondary) and then selling it as a drink (tertiary). Memorise PST (or think 'pst!') to describe the sequence a product goes through - Primary, Secondary, Tertiary.

So, key points to remember:

1. The primary sector is the extraction of raw materials, agriculture and fishing. The secondary sector is manufacturing. The tertiary sector is services to the public, which includes functions such as retail, transportation and restaurants.
2. An SME is a small to medium enterprise. The European Union defines an SME as having 250 employees or less. A micro-business has fewer than 10 employees. A multinational company (MNC) is a large company that operates within multiple countries.

Now ask yourself:

1. What are the advantages and disadvantages of being an SME?
2. What benefits do they bring to the economy?
3. Consider a vegetarian pizza sold at a supermarket. How could that product pass through the three sectors?

Now ask yourself (suggested answers):

1. What are the advantages and disadvantages of being an SME?

Advantages:
- More agile – able to make decisions easier and quicker as less people are needed to authorise them.
- Likely to have highly motivated staff as they will feel closer to the business.
- Many customers prefer to buy from SMEs as they are considered to pay greater attention to their needs.

Disadvantages:
- Will have less of a financial safety net, so will always face greater risks in challenging times and may find it harder to get funding.
- Lack the muscle and influence of large businesses, so will often lose out on contracts etc.
- Employing fewer staff makes them vulnerable to absences etc.

2. What benefits do they bring to the economy?

- 99% of businesses in the UK are SMEs, so they account for a large proportion of trade and taxation.
- As of 2015, they employ approximately 15.6 million UK workers, which is 60% of all private sector employees.
- They contribute to roughly 50% of all UK revenue generated.
- Their growth potential means many are the large companies of the future.
- In an economic downturn, many people who are made redundant choose to start their own businesses. So SMEs play a key role in moving an economy out of recession.

3. Consider a vegetarian pizza sold at a supermarket. How could that product pass through the three sectors?

Primary: The vegetables will need to be grown and picked.
Secondary: The pizza will then be assembled in a factory.
Tertiary: Besides retailing it through a supermarket, the food company may employ a marketing agency to promote their pizza range. As a service, this is also tertiary.

CHAPTER 12

Union Jack

I couldn't wait to get home and tell Mum how well it had gone with Alex. I hurried through the back door and into the kitchen with a broad grin on my face. Then I took one look at Mum and I could tell she had been crying.

"Mum, what's the matter?" I asked.

"Oh love, it's nothing," she said. She was hastily wiping her face and putting on a false smile, but it was too late.

"Don't be daft Mum, I can tell you've been crying. What's happened?"

"Nothing major, honestly. I just had a bad day at work, that's all."

"In what way was it bad?"

"I had my meeting with Jack, the Union Rep. He thinks the best way of us collectively keeping our jobs would be to put forward a counter-proposal accepting reduced hours. Maybe even consider a job share. But it would mean almost halving my hours and we just couldn't survive on that much income. So I just don't know what to do for the best."

Tears started to well up in her eyes, so I went over and gave her a big hug.

"The thing is, if I agree to that then I won't be granted any redundancy pay."

"So don't accept it then. They can't force you to reduce your hours like that."

"I know, but they're trying to find ways to change working practices to save money so we can stay. Jack said we have to be realistic and try to find a balance they will agree to."

"But that sounds like paying you less to do the same job! The job won't disappear, so it's not fair."

"I know love. I think the union are being a bit weak to be honest. They say they are just exploring possibilities right now. They call it *collective bargaining*."

"Collective bargaining?"

"It means trying to find a solution that works for as many as possible, in order to get an improved deal."

"Sounds like a way to fleece employees out of their jobs."

"To be fair, they present these options to us in private, but they would never agree to them in public. They are just trying to see what we would accept, before they go back with an offer."

"I hope you tell them you don't accept it?"

"He asked me whether I would be prepared to accept flexible working hours."

"How is flexible working hours any different from job share?"

"Well, there are times in the year when we are obviously a lot busier, so then I would do more hours, and work less hours when we are quiet."

"So, would you accept flexible working hours?"

"Not really. I explained that as my job is managerial, I am needed all the year around. I just plan my annual leave around our downtime periods. Then he raised the option of zero-hour contracts."

"Zero-hour contracts! But aren't they really unpopular with everyone?"

"Yes, but they have the advantage that I would probably still get more like my hours now."

"But then if you still end up working the same number of hours, surely that proves your job is needed?"

"I think that's what the union is getting at. Currently, the council is saying these jobs are no longer required. If they are prepared to accept people on zero-hour contracts, then they are effectively contradicting themselves."

"But surely they won't be that stupid?"

"Well, it's just a part of the negotiation at the end of the day. The council want to save money and the union want to save jobs."

"Oh Mum, I'm so sorry."

"Anyway, enough of me. How was your meeting with that boy from the university?"

"Oh, it went fine," I said, no longer wishing to sound too excited about it.

"Is he going to help you?"

"Kind of. It's not really help so much. In fact, I think it's more me helping him!"

"How's that?"

"Well, he's basically studying people who are starting out with a business idea. So he would be seeing what I do and whether it works or not."

"And have you agreed to that? It sounds like a TV documentary."

"Yes, I agreed. He's really nice and friendly." Mum had always been able to read my mind and knew immediately that I liked him.

"I hear from Aunt Kath that's he a nice looking boy?"

"Mum! It's purely professional!" And with that, I gave her another hug and said I was going to take a bath. She said I should do, while we can afford to pay for hot water.

What you've covered:

Theme	Amplification
Working practices	The meaning of flexible hours; part-time working; job sharing and zero-hour contracts.
Employer/employee relationships	The role of trade unions, including collective bargaining.

Memory hook: Union Jack

Union Jack proposed a change in working practices, including things like flexible working hours and job share as an alternative to potential redundancy for Lucinda's Mum. It's not always a negative option – for those people who have others commitments, such as studying or caring for relatives, it is a good way to remain employed.

So, key points to remember:

1. A trade union is an organisation whose members are workers of a particular industry or set of industries. Their role is to support its workers' rights by campaigning and negotiating with the employers on their behalf.
2. Collective bargaining is a process of negotiation that takes place over pay and other conditions of employment.
3. Setting up and making changes to working practices are part of the role of the Human Resource department.

Now ask yourself:

1. Can you think of any other examples of alternative working practices?
2. Do you think the Human Resources department is on the side of the employer or the employee?

Now ask yourself (suggested answers):

1.   **Can you think of any other examples of alternative working practices?**

   - Job rotation
   - Home working
   - Hot desking
   - Job sharing
   - Flexible hours
   - Part-time employment

2.   **Do you think the HR department is on the side of the employer or the employee?**

One of the key roles of the HR department is to ensure the employer complies with employment law. It is also their role to support the employees in ways to maximise their effectiveness and satisfaction. In some respects, that means they have to see both sides. However, ultimately they are employed by the organisation and will go up against the trade unions in times of dispute, on behalf of the organisation.

CHAPTER 13

Lucy and Brucie

I spent Friday night out with my best friend Lucy. I wanted to tell her all about my encounter with Alex. But she'd had a blazing row with her boyfriend Bruce, the night before. So, I ended up being her sounding board on how totally inept he was as a human being, while we downed various 2-for-1 cocktails. I'd told her all along that she shouldn't go out with anyone called Bruce on the general principle they would be commonly known as "Lucy and Brucie", which of course they were, but she was smitten. So that night, I was subjected to the juice on Bruce.

So, when Uncle Steve took Mum and I out to lunch the next day, I was a little the worse for wear. I managed to entertain them with stories of Bruce's exaggerated misdemeanours and casually mentioned my liaison with Alex.

Mum was determined that we were not to talk about her work situation, so Uncle Steve was keen to push forward my business idea as the light in an otherwise dark cave.

"I've got some good news for you, Lulu!" he announced suddenly.

"You've decided to have a hair transplant?" I blurted out immediately, without really thinking about its appropriateness.

Uncle Steve's casual "cheeky!" response was said simultaneously with Mum's "Lucinda!" I could tell she was less than amused.

"Sorry. Just a joke," I said guiltily.

"It's something better than improving the state of my *barnet* actually. You remember Brita, the lady that 'The Dragon' took you to meet?" I nodded eagerly, remembering the fantastic semi-mansion she lived in, whilst slapping his thigh for being mean to Aunt Kath.

"Well, she was so impressed with your business idea that she has found some fabric and made you two miniature duvet covers. One is a conventional cover and the other a better-looking alternative that follows your design."

"You're joking? That's amazing!" I said excitedly.

"Great, isn't it? What's more, she's got a granddaughter who has a miniature bed-set for one of her dolls. So she's made the duvet cover to fit the miniature duvet, which she's going to lend to you, along with the crib."

"Oh my God, that's so nice of her!"

"It means we can get moving on stage two of the operation."

"Which is what, exactly?"

"We need to take the product to market, of course!"

"How are we going to do that?"

"It's called *test marketing*, Lulu. We need to get a group of would-be customers together and pitch them the idea. Do you remember me telling you how Innocent Drinks started? How they took a load of sample product to a festival and got people to taste it?"

"I remember. They did a taste test and asked people whether they should give up their jobs to start the company by getting them to put their empty bottle in a 'yes' bin or a 'no' bin."

"That's it. Practically all the replies told them to give up their jobs, so they did. Well, that's an example of test marketing and I think it's time we did something similar."

"OK, but how am I going to do it exactly? I don't fancy pitching up at a festival with two miniature sized duvets and a doll's crib!"

"Not a festival, my girl! Remember when we discussed your target market? Most festival go-ers struggle to get into their sleeping bags, let alone make a bed."

"So, what exactly?"

"Well, we could start by getting some of your Aunt's book club members on board. They meet every other Monday. There's up to ten of them and they're all the right target demographic – mainly middle aged ladies, but a couple of blokes thrown in for good measure. Getting a group of people together to discuss a product or service is known as a *focus group*."

"Great! Why did my idea have to involve geriatric book clubs, when the Innocent Drinks people got music festivals?"

"Yeah, but they'll have got drenched and lost their car keys or something. Anyway, don't knock it 'til you've tried it, Lulu. Some of that book club stuff can get pretty racy!"

"I'll take your word for that, Uncle Steve! But seriously, won't they be biased? I mean, if they are Aunt Kath's friends and they know it's my idea, aren't they more likely to say they like it?"

"That's a good point, Lulu. We get around that by not saying anything about whose idea it is. We also obtain a baseline assessment in terms of their views on changing duvets."

"Baseline assessment?"

"It means we get them to complete a mini-survey first. So the survey would establish whether they use duvets or blankets. It would cover how often they change the bed, who does it and any problems they have doing it. Oh and where they tend to buy duvets from, so we understand their purchase mechanisms."

"But isn't everyone going to say they change the bed often? I mean, who is going to admit to changing their bed linen once a month? That would be too skanky to admit to, even in front of your 'racy' book club mates."

"Ha! You've got a talent for market research, Lulu! Well, I never change the bed, so what does that say about me?"

"It says you're useless around the house and poor Kath does everything," piped up my Mum.

"I'll choose to ignore that blatant defamation of character, Sis," he responded, whilst turning directly to me. "Yes, that's another form of bias. Few people admit to things they feel reflect badly on them socially. It's like the 'silent Tory' notion, where there are a proportion of Conservative voters who don't admit to it, so it skews the opinion polls."

"So, once we've gone through this baseline survey, then what do we do?"

"We'll get your Aunt to show them the duvet and the two covers and watch them discuss it. We'll say nothing about what it's about, as that will anchor them to positive messages and we'll see what it means to them."

"And we just sit in the room watching? Isn't that going to look a bit weird?"

"Nah, they'll forget we're there after two minutes. They ignore me every time I disturb their book debates anyway. At the end, we'll explain what it's all about and ask them the all important question."

"Which is?"

"Well, two questions actually. Firstly, whether they prefer it to the conventional duvet. Secondly, how much they would pay for one."

"Won't that depend on how much they pay now?"

"Yes, you are right! So we'll conceal the last two questions on the survey until after the discussion. Then they fill in those two questions based on what they've seen. Most people don't like sharing details on how much they pay for stuff, so we'll not get them to discuss that."

"Sounds like a good plan Uncle Steve, thanks!"

"It's Aunt Kath that has done all the donkey work. I can tell she really likes your idea and wants to see you give it a go."

"Where is Aunt Kath anyway?"

"She's gone over to see her cousin. He's got a few marital problems and needed some support. But on the way back, she's going to collect these duvet covers from Brita."

"Fab! When can I see them?"

"We'll pop around with them later tonight if you like?"

"Great!"

"Then we need to start thinking about how you're going to fund this."

"I know, but you told me to focus on researching the market Uncle Steve, so that's what I've been doing."

"Quite right too. But I think you need to start developing the business plan. I've got someone who might be able to help get it off the ground. He's a Business Angel."

"What's one of them?"

"It's someone who helps finance a project when conventional lending through banks is not available. They also help by providing their wisdom and opening them out to their network."

"Sounds too good to be true. Who is he?"

"He's a wonderful human being who should be treated with reverence at all times. It's me."

What you've covered:

Theme	Amplification
Marketing	Target marketing is about selecting which market segments to attract
Market Research	Test marketing involves offering prototypes of the product or service to a carefully selected sample of the market
Market Research	A sample is a group of people that are representative of the target population
Market Research	The importance of avoiding bias in market research
Finance	The meaning of the terms 'venture capital' and 'Business Angel'.

Memory hook: Lucy and Brucie

Use 'Lucy and Brucie' as an anchor for comparing two different prototypes. This is known as test marketing. It is important that the test is done on the right target market. Lucy and Brucie are not a good fit by name so they might not be the ideal target market for each other.

So, key points to remember:

1. For a target market to be attractive, it must generate a sufficient demand for sales, in order to generate a profit. However, this is relative to the sales price of the product being made. For example, few people can afford to buy a private jet, so their manufacturers may only produce a few hundred each year. The mark-up on a jet will therefore be high to account for such low sales volume. Imagine instead a toy jet, which sells for £20. If the market size for toy jets were as limited as real jets, then this price would clearly be insufficient to maintain the business.

2. The target market must also match the focus of the business. For example, children would probably not be within the target market of expensive artisan chocolates.

3. Venture capitalists are typically a pool of investors who invest collectively.

4. A Business Angel is a special example of venture capital. They are individuals who invest in businesses that are either new or require investment. Unlike crowdfunding, they will expect a return on their investment through a share of the business, which they could cash-in at a future exit point.

Now ask yourself:

1. How would you define the target markets for Primark and Debenhams?

2. What are the key factors to consider when defining the sample for a market research campaign?

3. What would you consider to be the advantages and disadvantages of venture capital as a means of obtaining funding?

Now ask yourself (suggested answers):

1. **How would you define the target markets for Primark and Debenhams?**

Primark are aimed at budget conscious shoppers who are less concerned with quality but want to follow the latest fashions. Their market could span a broad range of age groups. They would be more likely to attract female shoppers than male shoppers.

Debenhams focus more on quality, aiming at a slightly more affluent demographic. Their market is less likely to include young shoppers and may contain a higher share of male customers than Primark.

2. **What are the key factors to consider when defining the sample for a market research campaign?**

   - Is the sample a close match to the target market?
   - Will the sample size be large enough to adequately represent the target market population?
   - If the campaign were replicated again on another day, or in a different place, would it be likely to create similar results. In other words, is there a bias to this particular sample, such as interviewing people about their liking of chocolate, the day after Easter Sunday?

3. **What would you consider to be the advantages and disadvantages of venture capital as a means of obtaining funding?**

   Advantages:
   - They should benefit from the experience, network and advice the venture capitalist will provide.
   - The business won't have to pay interest on the money invested.

   Disadvantages:
   - They may lose some control and/or stake (in the form of shares) in the business.
   - Venture capitalists expect a significant return – often ten or more times their original investment.

CHAPTER 14

Book club focus group

On Monday, I received an email from Alex:

Dear Lucinda,

I hope you had a lovely weekend?

There is a guy coming to the University to deliver a talk this Wednesday and I think it might interest you. He is an expert on economics and his talk is on the economics of global businesses. It should be good — would you like to come?

If so, it's at 5pm. You can meet me in the main reception and we can go over together.

Best wishes,
Alex

I had something planned with my friend Susie on Wednesday, but after a couple of quick texts, it was moved and my acceptance email to Alex was sent.

The next big challenge was the focus group. Uncle Steve had brought the duvet cover samples around that evening and they were really well made. The only slight problem was the conventional duvet cover resembled a large pillowcase. It was actually quicker to put that one onto the doll's duvet than with my design, which kind of defeated the object! I did wonder if it would have been best to make a life size sample and demonstrate it for real?

However, I went around to their house after college. Aunt Kath had already set it up and Uncle Steve had created the questionnaire. At around 6pm the book reviewers started to arrive. There were ten of the 'racy' devils – a full house! They each carried their own little collection of books and I was slightly worried that my focus group would be a distraction from their real passion.

Thankfully, my worries were misplaced and by 6.15pm they were all assembled and keen to participate. Uncle Steve introduced it and made no reference to me. He also urged them to speak their mind and be honest about what they were going to be shown. This got them very excited, which then made me worry that revealing a doll's crib would be something of an anti-climax!

First of all, they completed the questionnaire, which only took around five minutes. Then the sheet that was covering the doll's crib was removed to reveal the conventional duvet. It reminded me of the TV show Dragon's Den. Uncle Steve demonstrated how we all accept this design into our lives before proposing another way. At this point, Aunt Kath introduced my design. To my immense relief, it seemed to be met with great enthusiasm!

All of the guests were then invited to take a look at the new design, try it out and discuss its practicality for a real life scenario.

They each got up and inspected both of the covers. I'd been told by Uncle Steve to write down as much of what we heard and saw as possible. I had asked whether we could film it on his video camera but he thought that might make them feel uncomfortable. So instead, I was busy writing.

Many of them commented on the quality of the stitching. I thought this was interesting as I had never inspected any bed linen for its stitching quality before – I guess we all kind of just assume it to be the case?

Then they discussed how different it would be to make a bed in that way. All of them thought it would be easier with my design, apart from one. She was adamant that her method for doing it was quicker, saying 'all this faffing around with press studs and buttons would drive me insane'. Then others started asking her about the technique, so she spent ages explaining it, which was really annoying! A couple of them started to agree that it might involve a bit more bending, which apparently is 'a big deal' at their age.

I had a couple who defended my idea as being much more practical. They agreed it took them ages to make their beds normally and that this would be a much easier way.

They focused heavily on whether the additional flaps on the three open sides, to conceal the buttons, would be impractical. The lady who was in favour of conventional duvets thought it might be uncomfortable. Nobody else could really understand what she meant as the flaps were on the sides and the bottom, so would never be in contact with their face, as she was implying. Those who were in favour of my design said the flaps actually added to its appearance and made it look better quality. This was the stage where the debate got most heated. If this was them being racy, then Uncle Steve had clearly lived a sheltered life!

A few minutes later, Uncle Steve brought it to a close and asked them to unfold a final piece of the questionnaire and complete the last two questions, which they did. Aunt Kath thanked them for their help and then introduced me and explained everything. This was really embarrassing as I could tell the lady who had been critical felt really bad. She apologised for being dismissive, but I said it was fine.

Uncle Steve and I then went into the dining room to discuss the results. He entered the questionnaire data into a spreadsheet, which he had set up on his laptop. All of the respondents were positive, except the one we knew about, and all of them apart from her had said they would prefer to buy my design! In fact, most of them said they would spend up to £10 more on my design, compared to what they would normally spend, which averaged out at £50.

"So, what I am entering here is mainly quantitative data," said Uncle Steve as he typed. "We designed the questionnaire so they had to tick certain boxes, such as 'how much they like changing bed linen on a scale of 1 to 10'. Because questions like this result in a number or category, we call it quantitative. The notes you made in terms of what they said individually, was unique from person to person. That is known as qualitative data."

It felt a bit like maths class in school all over again, but I was really interested in what Uncle Steve was teaching me, so I took it all in. However, I shared my concern that the sample might be a little biased, since they were all of a similar age and with the same kind of values.

"I agree, it probably wouldn't be ideal for a big company," said Uncle Steve. "But we don't have their budget for this kind of thing. In effect, what we have done is sampled from one particular demographic. In other words, they are not random. Ideally, we would have represented other age groups and perhaps more men. To do that properly, we would need to perform what's known as quota sampling, where you take a set number of people from different segments of your population. For example, you would include people from other age ranges and more males." He sketched something out on a piece of paper to illustrate his point.

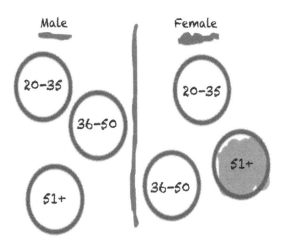

"So, say age and gender were our two criteria. Using quota sampling, we would include subjects from each of these six segments. The majority of our subjects today were from this segment here." He shaded in the circle representing older women. "But, I wouldn't worry about this right now. Besides, I think this may well be your target market."

A few minutes later, Uncle Steve said "Eureka!" excitedly. I turned to look at the computer screen.

"Look at this graph, Lulu! It confirms what we suspected. Our results show that the people you need to be targeting are indeed those who hate changing bed linen. I know it seemed obvious to us, but now we have proof in numbers."

He was pointing at a graph that plotted the scores on two different questions.

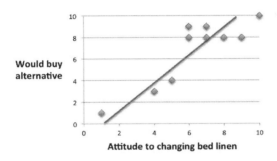

"So, you can see there is a strong positive correlation between 'attitude towards changing bed linen' and 'liking your product'. The people who love changing linen were a bit nonplussed with your idea. But those who hate it will be your first customers. Now, we just need to identify all of the other people in the world who hate changing duvet covers, and this time next year Rodney, we'll be millionaires!"

"What about that lady who said she didn't use duvets on her bed?" I asked.

"I've taken her out. She is what's known as an outlier – someone who is not representative of the population we are targeting. Although maybe your design could convert her!"

Aunt Kath came in to join us and gave me a big pat on the back. We all agreed it was a great success. Now my job was to type up my notes so they could be added as an appendix to the business plan.

What you've covered:

Theme	Amplification
Market Research	The distinction between qualitative and quantitative data
Market Research	The difference between random sampling and quota sampling
Market Research	The concept of correlation

Memory hook: Book club focus group

Think of Aunt Kath's book club members as a sample of a population. If the sample represents all of the market segments being sold to, then that is fine. However, if other segments are not represented in the sample, then the results cannot inform on what they may think or want. In this case, most of the sample were females, aged 50+.

So, key points to remember:

1. Qualitative data is often descriptive. It could be the box people write additional comments in on a survey, or a transcript of a conversation.
2. Quantitative data is either in numerical form or categories that can be counted. So whilst 'male' and 'female' are categories, it is possible to count the number of subjects in each category.
3. Correlation measures the strength of relationship between two variables. If the relationship is strongly positive, then the score will be close to 1. If the relationship is strongly negative (i.e. when one variable is high, the other is low) the score will be close to -1. No relationship results in a score close to zero.

Now ask yourself:

1. Can you think of real-life examples of: (i) positively correlated variables, (ii) negatively correlated variables and (iii) variables with no correlation?
2. Pivoting is the name given to a company changing some aspect of its business in a fundamental way. Can you think of any real-life examples of pivoting that worked or didn't work?

Now ask yourself (suggested answers):

1. **Can you think of real-life examples of: (i) positively correlated variables, (ii) negatively correlated variables and (iii) variables with no correlation?**

    Positive: Outdoor temperature and sales of ice cream – people are more likely to buy ice cream in hot weather.
    Negative: 'Driver age' and the price of car insurance premiums - the older people become, the more likely their premiums are to reduce.
    No correlation: Volume of shoe sales and regions of the country - we all require shoes.

2. **Pivoting is the name given to a company changing some aspect of its business in a fundamental way. Can you think of any real-life examples of pivoting that worked or didn't work?**

    a. **Coca-Cola** – in 1985, Coca-Cola changed the taste of their drink through the introduction of 'New Coke'. This was in reaction to the growing popularity of Pepsi, evidenced through blind taste tests. The market rejected 'New Coke' with severe consequences for the company. Within three months, it was forced to re-introduce the original formulation under the brand name 'Coke Classic'. By 1992, 'New Coke' had disappeared altogether.

    b. **Wrigley** - Wrigley didn't initially sell chewing gum. William Wrigley Jr. was a soap and baking powder salesman who had the idea of offering free chewing gum with his purchases. When it proved to be more popular than his actual product, Wrigley went on to manufacture his own chewing gum. Today, the company grosses billions in revenue and is one of the most recognisable brands in American history.

    c. **Twitter** – originally called Odeo, it began life as a network where people could find and subscribe to podcasts. However, when Apple incorporated podcast technology into their phones, the market potential for Odeo nose-dived. The founders asked its employees to come up with new ideas. They consequently decided to change direction entirely (i.e. pivot) and run with the idea of a micro-blogging platform, allegedly conceived by Jack Dorsey and Biz Stone. Subsequently, Twitter was born.

Due to a minor emergency with my outfit choice, I was running late to meet Alex on the Wednesday and a little worried he might assume I wasn't coming and go to the talk without me. So when I got to reception at a quarter past five, I was so relieved to see him still there waiting for me.

"I'm so sorry!" I said, doing an awkward mini-run as I approached. "I got caught up with a friend who needed my advice on something." I've always been a terrible liar, as I immediately go bright red, which is a dead giveaway to anyone that knows me.

"Don't worry, I was running late myself, so I've not long got here," was his reply. I might have been mistaken, but it looked like he was lying about that also.

As we walked through various corridors and out into little gardens, Alex told me about the guy who was giving the talk. He was a leading expert in economics, but became increasingly frustrated that all the stuff he was working on had no relevance to the real world. So he decided to spend a year travelling the globe, discovering how economics affects real communities. Since his return, he has been on a tour around Europe describing his experiences. It was a big deal that he was talking at the university and the tickets were in hot demand.

When we arrived at the venue, Alex presented two tickets to the lady at the front desk and we walked through into the lecture theatre. The room was packed and most of the seats were taken. Luckily, Alex spotted two spaces together near the back. "Come on," he said, and grabbed my hand to lead me through the barricade of people. I squeezed his hand gently and felt a surge of energy from the touch.

"I hope you didn't mind me grabbing your hand just then?" he asked nervously, as we took our seats.

"I'm glad you did, otherwise I'd have lost you for sure," I replied. We looked at each other and our gaze seemed to remain that little bit longer than was necessary. I felt myself going red and, as if aware of my discomfort, Alex started rifling through his bag before bringing out a notebook. Damn, I hadn't come prepared to take any notes.

"Oops! In my mad rush, I completely forgot to bring anything to write with."

"Was that the mad rush with your friend?" Alex asked mischievously. I felt he'd seen through my white lie.

"Yes of course," I replied guiltily.

"Don't worry, I'll take notes for both of us." He nudged my leg with his knee, but after the nudge our legs were still gently touching, even though they didn't need to be. Right the way through the talk, I was aware of our legs being in contact and didn't, for one moment, want to move an inch. Concentrating on the talk of the economics expert was going to be an act of extreme discipline!

Fortunately, his lecture was completely beguiling and for that whole hour, I was totally absorbed in the stories coming at me.

He began his talk by explaining the accepted wisdom of economics, specifically about keeping everything in balance, which they refer to as equilibrium. He put weighing scales with two arms on the table at the front of the room. In front of each arm he added two large pieces of card, labelled 'supply' and 'demand'. "So we, as consumers, have a demand for products and services. Let's suppose that all of us here today are a community of fanatical apple eaters. The growers of apples satisfy our demand by supplying us with what we need." To illustrate his point, he put two apples on either side of the weighing scales. After a bit of two-ing and fro-ing, the scales balanced. "Providing everything stays in balance, all is fine with the world.

"But what if we tell all our friends about the wonderful taste of apples and they decide to join us? Suddenly we have created more demand than the poor growers can cope with." He paused and removed the apple from the supply side of the scales. They tipped over. He pointed at the apple on the demand side. "If we, as consumers, want more than suppliers can handle, there is imbalance. Ask any child who doesn't get the number one selling toy of the year for Christmas. Ask people during a war to explain why rationing of produce has affected how much their family can eat.

"But let's look at it from the other perspective. What if the apple growers anticipate a surge in demand that never materialises? Now, supply outstrips demand." He returned the apple to the supply side and removed the apple from demand, whilst pointing at the supply apple. "Businesses have stock they can't shift, car repair companies have mechanics sitting around doing nothing. Governments have mountains of sugar or milk that nobody can consume.

"And we see this in action every day. Airbus and Boeing have been happily making large scale jet airplanes for decades. They have had the market sewn up; effectively just competing with each other. Their scales had Airbus on one side and Boeing on the other. Their primary objective was tipping the scales in their favour. Now what has happened? New market entrants have come along. The Canadian aircraft manufacturer Bombardier has begun competing directly with them. Entrants from China have entered the fray. Suddenly, Airbus and Boeing are together at one end of the scales and the new entrants are together at the other. Suddenly Airbus and Boeing are thinking: 'if this is what real competition is like, give us the good old days of us versus them any day'.

"You see it in the commercial world every day. Back in 2009, Audi launched a billboard to promote their new design with the words – 'Your move, BMW'. Some months later, BMW responded with a billboard of their own - 'Checkmate'.

In 2016, BMW will celebrate a centenary of being in existence. It wouldn't surprise me one bit if Audi, or Mercedes-Benz, publicly thank them for one hundred years of competition. Thanking their rival for competition! Why would any company do that? Because the real competition is not BMW, it's the other manufacturers around the world who are the competition. Let's be Mercedes-Benz for a moment. If we tell the world it's just 'us' and 'them', maybe the rest will go away? And then we can go back to telling the world how we're better than them after all.

"As we all know, the world of economics is about studying how all of this fits together in the big picture. The German government wants Mercedes, Audi, Porsche and BMW to sew up the competition because each and every vehicle they sell provides tax revenue for the German government. Do they want Toyota and Chevrolet importing their cars into Germany? Of course they don't, so they charge import duty to balance out what they have lost in tax revenue. Or they get Toyota and Chevrolet to build factories in Germany, so they employ German workers, who in turn pay them income tax."

He pointed at the scales again. "Balance. It's all about balance. And then we throw price into the mix. Going from two providers of aircraft to six creates intense competition. The problem is, when each aircraft costs so much in time and effort to make, you can't afford to discount them too much. Doing a 'buy one, get one free' offer in the aircraft industry puts you on the runway to financial ruin. There is precious little elasticity in the supply side of aircraft. In other words, a one percent reduction in price is unlikely to result in a ten percent increase in demand." Picking up a model aircraft, he tried stretching it to prove his point. The audience laugh.

"Do we all understand about price elasticity of demand?" There were a few shaking heads, so he began writing on a white board. "OK, let me explain.

$$\text{Price elasticity of demand} = \frac{\text{Percentage change in quantity demanded}}{\text{Percentage change in price}}$$

"For some products, a change in price, either up or down, has very little affect on demand. We're all apple fanatics remember? So if the growers raise the price of apples, it's still not going to stop us buying, because for us, there is no alternative. That is inelasticity. Milk is inelastic. Electricity is inelastic. Cigarettes were inelastic for years. Vapes will become inelastic.

"Other markets are more elastic." To prove his point, he produced a pair of socks and underpants, which created a further ripple of laughter around the theatre. "We all need these right? So, if we all need them and they don't cost too much to buy, doesn't that make them inelastic also?"

He stretched a sock and it expanded. "Guess what – it turns out they're pretty elastic! Maybe there's a global shortage of cotton due to bad weather in cotton producing countries the year before? The availability of cotton reduces, so the price they charge for their cotton goes up. Maybe the government introduces a living wage hike in the hourly rate companies must pay their workers. So again, the price goes up.

"But we all need clothes don't we? So will we keep buying them regardless of price? Not necessarily. Ah, go with me on this one, for a moment," he added, noting a few dissenting heads in the audience.

"In a real crisis, we can choose not to buy them at all and make do with what we've got. We can give our old ones to our mums to mend for us. Because we all know men are incapable of sewing, right! It's called 'darning'. This is an alternative. It's what we know and understand as a 'substitute'. So now, people across the world are mending their own socks. That makes them elastic. And it turns out that the criteria for deciding whether something is elastic or not, is that equation I just drew for you. If the result is greater than 1 then the product is elastic because a change in price affects the change in quantity more. If it is less than one, then the product is inelastic.

"But here's the really interesting thing. Let's suppose we're not buying our socks in the same quantities as we did before. Instead, we are darning our old ones. Which means the demand for needles and rolls of cotton goes up, which enables them to raise their prices. The impact of a change in demand for one product can have a radical affect on others. You see, economics is not just about keeping apples in equilibrium. It's about everything – pears, bananas, even socks and underpants!"

It was an absorbing talk and the whole room was captivated.

"Now, I spent a lot of years of my life studying the mathematics of all this. I was curious to see how everything affected government decisions. This was the world of macroeconomics. All of the things that take place in the countries around the world – from the production of aircraft and luxury cars to everyday items like socks and underpants, all sum together to create a macro economy. And people in government, or Whitehall for us in the UK, make it their job to ensure everything balances. Because when it goes out of balance, things go wrong. Businesses go bust, which means people lose their jobs, so unemployment starts to rise. A rise in unemployment means the government has to tax those who are still in a job more, to cover the lost income for the unemployed. And when people get taxed more, guess what? They spend less with businesses, who aren't then able to employ the people out of work. Argh! It's a whole big mass of balance. A huge machine, of which we are all tiny cogs, washers and bolts, holding it all together.

"And then one day, I woke up and thought about the people who are a tiny part of the machine. When you live in the world of economics, you only see the bigger picture. If someone loses his or her job in Sheffield, it doesn't change things one jot, because the machine is enormous. But to that one person in Sheffield, their world has changed beyond belief. And then I thought beyond Sheffield to other parts of the world. In other words, I thought about the micro economy – the little cogs and washers that combine together to create the macro economy.

"It's then I realised something. I needed to go and see it for myself. Right away. It simply couldn't wait. So I did. I spoke to my boss and told her I wanted to take a twelve-month sabbatical to go around the world and study the micro economy at large.

"In those twelve months, I have met people and seen things in all corners of the globe. I've seen a little factory making refrigeration units in East Timor. I've met fishermen off the Atlantic coast in Alaska. And I've spoken to qualified doctors doing hair transplants in Istanbul." My mind shifted to Uncle Steve for a moment.

"All of it has altered my perspective on economics in a way I could never have imagined. The things that hold true for the macro economy, particularly in the Western hemisphere, bear no resemblance to what goes on in day-to-day lives around the world. And that's what I'm going to share with you today."

Wow, I had no idea economics could be so fascinating! And through all of this, I had totally forgotten that Alex's leg was still pressed gently into mine.

What you've covered:

Theme	Amplification
Markets	What is meant by demand, supply and equilibrium
Markets	The importance of demand and supply to consumers and businesses
Markets	The factors that lead to a change in demand and supply
Markets	How changes in demand and supply can impact price and quantity
Markets	The difference between the macro and micro economy
Markets	The concept of price elasticity of demand

Memory hook: Balancing apples

The weighing scales containing apples is a great way to understand the supply and demand equation and the need for equilibrium. Remember the equation for price elasticity of demand:

Price elasticity of demand = (% change in quantity) / (% change in price)

Or memorise: "PED is PCQ over PCP".

So, key points to remember:

1. Price elasticity of demand measures how likely it is that a change in the price of a product or service will influence customers' likelihood to continue purchasing.
2. If a product or service rises in price, and is still in demand at the same level as before, then it is said to be price inelastic. This would lead to a PED value of _less_ than 1.
3. If demand for a product or service falls in percentage terms following a rise in price, then it is said to be price elastic. Customers are not prepared to pay higher prices. This would lead to a PED value of _greater_ than 1.
4. Inelastic products can: have a strong brand name; be expensive to switch from or have a powerful USP.
5. Elastic products may have plenty of substitutes or could be nearing the end of their product life cycle.

Now ask yourself:

1. Is petrol considered price elastic or inelastic? What about holidays to a particular country, for example Mexico?
2. Why is knowledge of 'price elasticity of demand' important to businesses?
3. What would happen if the availability of milk reduced?
4. What is meant by an 'oligopoly'?

Now ask yourself (suggested answers):

1. **Is petrol considered price elastic or inelastic? What about holidays to a particular country, for example Mexico?**

    Petrol is price inelastic. Most people are forced to purchase petrol, irrespective of its price. So if the cost of petrol rises, the volume of petrol consumed is relatively unaffected.

    A Mexican holiday would be price elastic since there is adequate choice of other destinations. If the cost of holidays to Mexico increased dramatically, perhaps due to a political or currency crisis, people would likely go elsewhere.

2. **Why is knowledge of 'price elasticity of demand' important to businesses?**

    It is important for businesses to understand the reaction of their customers to price changes. It also enables them to detect opportunities in other industries that have been affected by price elasticity. For example, tourist destinations outside of Mexico could take advantage of their situation.

3. **What would happen if the availability of milk reduced?**

    Milk would then become a scarce resource and its price would go up. People would either consume less milk or use substitute products such as soya milk. However, an increase in milk prices would probably cause soya to increase in price also.

4. **What is meant by an 'oligopoly'?**

    An oligopoly is a market dominated by a small number of companies. In this situation, the market is said to be highly concentrated. However, a number of small-scale businesses may also exist. For example, the Travelodge and Premier Inn hotel chains dominate the market for UK business travellers. In addition, guesthouses and bespoke hotels will also compete for trade. These are the small-scale businesses.

CHAPTER 16

Boda-Boda

The second half of the economics talk was even more absorbing than the first. This is how his story unfolded.

"I began my trip in East Timor. You might be asking yourself where East Timor is and why I started my journey there? Well it's a country in the South East Asia region that borders Indonesia. It was originally a Portuguese colony, but following independence, became taken over by its neighbours Indonesia. This was a terrible period in its history as it was a bloody and painful affair. In 2002 it regained its independence, but the country had been ripped apart by years of suppression.

"It is the aftermath of these tragic events that make East Timor interesting from an economic perspective. You see, the country can lay claim to having one of the strangest statistics in any study of global economics you will find. Anywhere. Take a look at this graph.

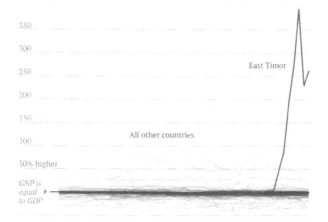

"So this graph compares the ratio of GNP to GDP across all countries of the world. As I am sure you will all know, GDP stands for Gross Domestic Product and effectively measures the output of the country as a whole. So the sum of all outputs, from cars built, to computers assembled, to hotels accommodated. Each dollar or euro that every company earns, contributes towards their country's GDP.

"And GNP? Well, it stands for Gross National Product. For most countries, it's actually very similar to GDP. As the thick black line on this graph demonstrates, the difference between the two is mostly negligible. The key difference is those words 'domestic' and 'national'. So if a country earns or receives additional money from abroad, then it is counted in GNP, but not GDP."

There were murmurs of recognition, as people around the theatre suddenly understood the graph. I was still a little perplexed.

"Ah, I see many of you are now realising why East Timor is something of an anomaly! Over the last decade or so, its GNP has been anything from 100% to 350% greater than its GDP. How could this happen? It's almost absurd, right?

"Well not quite. You see, East Timor is unfortunately a country with low production in anything and extremely poor economic performance. But what it does benefit from, to a very significant extent, is overseas aid. Countries all around the world contribute towards helping East Timor get back on its feet. In fact, at 350% we all collectively give East Timor three and a half times more than it makes on its own.

"Which is good and bad in equal measure. Good of course, because we are supporting its development following a long and painful period of crisis. Bad, in that the country needs this level of support at all. It's effectively on an economic life support machine. Living in East Timor right now cannot be much fun. And that's what I wanted to see for myself.

"Now, getting there is not easy. This is not New York. There are no direct British Airways or Emirates flights scheduled to East Timor. My journey took over a day and a half, which included three stops. But get there I did.

"There is one thing I should explain about my trip. I didn't have an itinerary. I also didn't have anyone waiting for me at the airport holding a piece of card with my surname on it. And I certainly didn't have any whirlpool baths in the penthouse suite of a multinational hotel chain to look forward to. So, I arrived in East Timor with no place to live and no plan of what to do next. And that's how I met Desmond.

"From my arrival at the airport, I took a cab into the centre of its capital city, which is called Dili. Yes they have cabs, although don't expect electric windows and air-con. I asked the driver to take me to a hotel. His English wasn't great, but he understood what I was asking for and looked very worried. Unbeknown to me, I had arrived in East Timor at a time when there was a huge NGO and IGO conference taking place.

"He took me to a hotel, but instead of dropping me off, simply said 'wait here'. He went inside and two minutes later came out looking concerned. 'Hotel full,' he said. 'You stay with me tonight.' Now I tried to gesticulate with him, as I am sure you would if a taxi driver in a strange country insisted you stay with him for the night. But he was insistent, and it was late. So twenty minutes later, I arrive at his home, which contained his wife and two children. He had to get back on the road to earn some more money, so I was left in the charge of his wife, who I now know as Amy. Crazy right? Who would do that over here? None of you? Quite right too.

"Now I won't go into the details of my stay with Desmond and Amy. It was basic and I had an uncomfortable night's sleep. But it was the kindest act of unconditional welfare I have ever received in my life and probably ever will receive. And this was from two people who, by our standards, were destitute. I did leave them the following day and found a backpacker's hostel, but some weeks later, once I had wised up to the country that was now my temporary home, I returned with a small, but in their world, most generous gift.

"What did I learn from my time in East Timor? Well, this is a country undergoing significant social and economic change. Prices of what we would consider everyday commodities are outside the reach of most citizens. A large IGO community has been created to provide all of the overseas aid on the ground. The term IGO you will know I'm sure - it stands for Inter-Governmental Organisation. IGOs are groups created to provide solutions and support, funded by governments, but operating independently of them. Organisations such as UNESCO and UNICEF are good examples. So these IGOs inadvertently create a market that local retailers can inflate. Which means the prices of many everyday goods are simply unaffordable for most citizens of East Timor.

"In addition to the economic change, they have huge social change taking place. People want to move to the cities where there are jobs and prospects. This means they are experiencing what we refer to as *urbanisation*. But the cities are not set up to cope with this influx of people and their infrastructure and services simply cannot cope. This phenomenon is not restricted to East Timor. As you will know, urbanisation has been taking place on a frightening scale in China and India for the last few decades. But it is taking place in other regions too. Significantly, East Timor does not have the financial resources to cope with this level of social change.

"And what of technology change? Well, East Timor is trying to act like a first world country. The IGO and NGO workers need broadband. They want connectivity with the rest of the world. But the country is fifteen years behind the rest of the world on this, at least. So again, demand is outstripping supply.

"What does this mean for its inhabitants? Is it making them angry? Revolt? Resort to crime? In fact, quite the reverse. One of the great strengths the country has is a deep underlying moral code. The type of code that instructs Amy and Desmond to take a complete stranger into their home. Even if it puts their own family's personal safety at risk.

"For sure, the problems East Timor is encountering now are nothing compared to the crises during its military occupation by Indonesia. Independence has given its people freedom. But it has also created new problems. Problems caused bizarrely by the goodwill of first world countries providing it with aid. Macroeconomics has microeconomic implications.

"So, where should I go from East Timor? Well to my mind, the natural next step was somewhere that had experienced similar issues to East Timor, but is now on an upward trajectory. Africa.

"I arrived in Uganda, a country that had itself gone through civil war and experienced widespread genocide. That was back in the late seventies and three decades of political unrest followed. A country that has received generous levels of foreign aid, just like East Timor. But a country now classified as one of the world's 'developing nations'.

"Yet the difference between a 'developing country' and a 'developed country' couldn't be starker. In 2014, the GDP of Uganda reached a record high of 27 billion US dollars. Yet this still represents just 0.04% of the world's economy, despite having a larger population than Canada." There were sharp intakes of breath. "I know right! Canada: two percent of the world's GDP, making them the tenth richest nation on the planet. Each day, the average Canadian generates somewhere around fifty times the revenue as the average Ugandan. Staggering. And yet, the gap between them is slowly narrowing. Slowly.

"So, how has Uganda managed to achieve this level of progress? Well, like much of East and Central Africa, it took the overseas aid it received and utilised it. One of the keys to its success has been the creation of social enterprises. Perhaps a pivotal difference with our understanding of social enterprise is that theirs mostly operate on a 'for-profit' basis. In Africa, there is no barrier between having a social purpose and making profit.

"Let me tell you about one very interesting enterprise I met. Its name is *Tugende*. When I said Uganda was a developing country, that shouldn't mask the fact that living conditions over there are still light years away from the conditions we consider normal in the West. Sixty five percent of the population survive on less than two dollars per day.

"In Kampala, the nation's capital, they also have a taxi system. Like East Timor, it doesn't comprise of the Mercedes and BMWs we enjoy here. But what they do have are *boda-boda*, or just *boda* for short. It's basically a motorcycle with a passenger seat. And there are lots of them. The typical income for a boda driver is around five dollars per day, so more than twice the national average. Which makes it quite a desirable occupation, particularly amongst young men. But herein lay the problem the country faced: the drivers of these vehicles don't own the boda themselves. They rent them from landlords who can withdraw the boda, or inflate prices, at any time.

"So what's going on here from an economic perspective? Well it comes back to supply, demand and equilibrium again, I'm afraid. There are lots of young men in Uganda that want the boda career. Demand therefore outstrips supply. Which means the landlords can, at any one time, collect their boda and issue them to other wannabe drivers at a higher price. They effectively own the supply.

"*Tugende* was set up to address this social problem. They have created a programme that enables drivers to own their own boda in around two years, through a lease and repayment system. They also receive driver training as part of the package, which improves safety, both for them and pedestrians.

"This vital enterprise gives the young men of Kampala and beyond, the opportunity to build a sustainable life for themselves and their family. Drivers of boda are wealthy by Ugandan standards. Gradually and progressively, with enterprises like *Tugende*, Uganda is emerging from the rubble left by the Idi Amin dictatorship. Macroeconomics has microeconomic implications.

"From Uganda I moved across Africa, travelled through areas of South America and up into Central America. But I want to end my story in somewhere completely different. In fact, about as far removed from the scenery and issues of Central Africa as you can get. That place is Alaska.

"For those of you that have never had the fortune to go there, this is one of the most unspoilt and beautiful places on earth. It is America's 49th state and on that basis, has security that Africa can only dream of.

"Does that mean it doesn't have economic problems? Absolutely not. Can anyone tell me what the most significant industry is in Alaska?"

A pause. Someone shouted out "logging".

"Logging is certainly a key industry in Alaska. This is very much a region built on the primary industry. But perhaps what is even more significant is its fishing industry. Alaska provides the United States with more fish than any other state or country in the world. Many Alaskan families depend upon its seas for a livelihood. So, as well as being dependent upon Mother Nature, it is also totally subservient to the policy making of Federal Government.

"Now, a significant change was made to the American fishery policy recently. It didn't make headline news over here, but they certainly know about it in Alaska. Historically, fishermen in Alaska could fish without limits. This has led to concern over fish stocks. Specifically, there is concern that they are fishing at a faster rate than the fish stocks are replenishing. Consequently, certain fish species are becoming depleted. So the government has passed a law that limits the number of fish that can be taken from the sea.

"This law, which means nothing to most of us, has had huge implications on those Alaskan fishermen. Many of them have seen their wages drop significantly. And in a country where the average earnings are around fifty five thousand dollars per annum, they typically earn less than thirty thousand. In the Yukon Delta region, that figure reduces to nearer twenty thousand.

"By Ugandan standards these people are living a lavish lifestyle of excess. But by American standards, they are substantially poorer than the average. Albeit their cost of living is lower compared to the densely populated cities in other states.

"I raise this issue with you because it brings home what I had hoped to achieve from my trip perfectly. Governments are faced with making difficult decisions. In just about every case, the implications of those decisions create winners and losers simultaneously. Raising interest rates benefits savers, but penalises those seeking debt. The winners of this particular decision lie out to sea on the Alaskan coast. This was an environmental decision. However, the decision also had serious repercussions on thousands of people living across the state of Alaska. Macroeconomics has microeconomic implications.

"I could tell you stories from several other countries. I visited Venezuela, which is currently dealing with huge problems of its own political making. As many of you studying business will know, Venezuela has the highest level of inflation of any country across the world right now. Its economy is in meltdown and it's a fascinating case. Hugo Chavez, its previous president, put in place socialist interventions that have now crippled the nation's economy. The country relies heavily upon its vast oil reserves, which should make them one of the world's richest nations. In fact, much of their oil goes directly to China, to pay its debt to them. What's more, as we all know from our visits to the petrol station, oil is one of the most volatile commodities across the world. Its price can change dramatically from one year to the next. Yet it is also one of the most price inelastic products. We all depend upon oil for our cars and our heating, no matter what the price. And this has hurt the people of Venezuela greatly.

"But they have other problems, again of the government's creation. They made the mistake of creating different exchange rates for imported goods compared to the price of products in the country. This hugely de-valued their currency, called the bolivar. A year ago, one United States dollar equalled 175 bolivars. As of today, one dollar is worth a thousand bolivars. This means that most everyday products are too expensive for anyone holding bolivars, which just happens to be its citizens. What's the cost of a pint of milk in the UK today? Fifty pence? Imagine in one year's time, the value of the pound changing so much that a pint of milk costs five pounds. A loaf of bread ten pounds. That is what the people in Venezuela are facing today. I repeat again, macroeconomics has microeconomic implications.

"Thank you for listening."

What you've covered:

Theme	Amplification
Economics	The meaning of GDP and GNP
Political	The meaning of Non-Governmental Organisation (NGO) and Inter-Governmental Organisation (IGO)
Social	How demographic changes such as urbanisation can affect the lives of everyday people
Political	How political decisions can affect business activity
Political	Why governments regulate business activity
Economic	The importance of exchange rates to a country's financial health

Memory hook: Boda-Boda

Use the image of a taxi in the form of a motorbike to recall how supply and demand affects peoples' lives and how social enterprises can be created to improve things for the better. Supply and demand challenges exist in all countries, from the poorest (East Timor) to the richest (Alaska, US).

So, key points to remember:

1. Gross Domestic Product provides a summary of how much income a country is generating. When an economy is growing, GDP will usually rise.
2. Political decisions greatly affect how countries perform. Venezuela is an example of a country in turmoil through bad political decision-making.
3. When the value of a currency rises against other currencies, it becomes more expensive to live. So when you go from needing 175 bolivars to buy a dollar, to needing over 1,000, your currency is effectively worthless in real terms.

Now ask yourself:

1. Which country currently has the greatest GDP and how does the UK compare against other countries?
2. How do political decisions affect life here in the UK?
3. How has the rate of the pound against the dollar and the euro changed over the last few years and what impact does this have on us as citizens?

Now ask yourself (suggested answers):

1. **Which country currently has the greatest GDP and how does the UK compare against other countries?**

    As of 2015, the United States had the highest global GDP at $17,968 billion. This accounted for 23% of the world's GDP. The UK was fifth with $2,865 billion, representing 4% of the total. China, Japan and Germany were the other three countries with higher GDP.

2. **How do political decisions affect life here in the UK?**

    Political decisions will affect the economy and therefore people's lives in a variety of ways. For example:
    - Changes in tax rates will make people worse or better off.
    - Decisions to cut spending can cause people to lose jobs.
    - The passing of new laws changes how people live, for example same-sex marriage.
    - New investment strategies can influence where businesses locate their head offices or new factories, which will create or lose jobs. As way of example, consider the proposed 'Northern Powerhouse' and the High Speed 2 (HS2) railway line.

3. **How has the rate of the pound against the dollar and the euro changed over the last few years and what impact does this have on us as citizens?**

    Since the financial crisis of 2007/08, the pound improved on the euro, meaning that the pound was worth more euros. However, the decision to exit the EU meant the value of the pound dropped sharply against the euro and the dollar, so the pound was worth less. This affects people who go on holiday abroad since their pound buys them less foreign currency. When a currency rises in value against others, it is referred to as being "strong". When it falls it "weakens".

    To understand the implications of this, imagine a UK company importing a widget from Germany, which costs €2. Suppose the exchange rate last year was £1=€2. This meant the widget cost £1 to buy. Now suppose the pound weakens dramatically, so that £1 is only worth €1. Nothing has changed in the German economy - for them it is still worth €2. But for the UK company, that widget is now costing them £2 in real terms. So it has doubled in price.

CHAPTER 17

Angry Frank

After the talk, Alex asked me if I fancied a drink at the local pub he frequented with his university mates. I met his work roommate Natasha. She was there with her boyfriend, who was called Frank. I felt a surge of relief seeing there was clearly nothing between her and Alex.

They were all talking about the economics talk and found it as enthralling as I did.

"I guess it all comes down to change, really," said Frank.

"How do you mean?" asked Alex.

"Well, all of the countries he visited have gone through extensive change. It's the impact of change that's the problem. When things change, people have new problems to cope with."

"I guess so. But the problems the people in those countries are facing are all external to them. The decisions made by the Venezuelan government. The American government. The foreign aid provided to East Timor. None of it is within the control of the people. At least at a micro level, people who create a business own their destiny by implementing their own form of change. Internal change."

Frank shook his head. "But that's not true. There will be plenty of businesses in Venezuela that have gone bust because of the decisions made by Chavez. They may have been brilliant businesses that were creating lots of positive internal change. But their whole business has been wiped out by events outside of their control. In the world of rock, paper, scissors, external change beats internal change any day of the week."

Alex looked dismissively at Frank's argument. "Venezuela is an extraordinary case. That's an example of a country outside of equilibrium. For most countries of the world, business owners are masters of their own destiny."

"But how do you know that yesterday's Venezuela couldn't be the United Kingdom tomorrow? Or France? Germany? At any single point in time, the whole global economy can come down like a pack of cards. Surely you haven't forgotten the financial crisis of 2007? You are a business expert after all?!" It was clear there was some on-going tension between Frank and Alex.

"Yes, but developed countries belong to a stable economic system," replied Alex calmly. "Collectively, we overcame the financial crisis of 2007. Venezuela doesn't belong and is therefore vulnerable to bad governmental decision-making. In the grand scheme of things, East Timor and Uganda are going through Lewin's three step model of change, but on a larger scale."

"Here you go again with your theory, Alex! What exactly does Lewin's model of change have to do with East Timor?"

"Well, they've just been unfrozen. That period of unfreezing has created instability and uncertainty, but also a platform for change."

I had no idea what this meant, so I piped up the courage to ask. "What exactly is this model of unfreezing?"

Alex gave me an encouraging look. "So, there is a famous guy called Kurt Lewin, who created this three step model of change. For an organisation to change itself radically, it must first put a stop to every bad behaviour and bad idea it had before. This is known as unfreezing. Then it must initiate the change it needs. That is the changing stage. Finally, it must make those changes permanent by embedding them as the norm. That's known as the refreezing stage."

"Your problem, Alex, is that you are too ideological," continued Frank. "You see business as this entity that can just be fixed with some magic wand. The reality is that companies don't have that degree of control on their destiny. Like the guy kept saying, 'macroeconomics has microeconomic implications'."

"But if you took that view, Frank, business owners would never make any decisions of their own. They would be too scared to make any planned change because they'd be waiting for the unplanned change to hit them. Yes recessions happen, rises in tax, unemployment and exchange rates happen. They're all part of the business cycle. I get that. But if they let it control their whole way of thinking, then the country as a whole would never have any form of innovation and they'd create the situation of doom you are describing, all by themselves."

"I think you have to agree he's got you there, Frank!" said a guy called Elliot who had been quiet until then.

"So you just ignore everything the expert said tonight?" said Frank desperately. He was going quite red in the face.

"No, everything he said made sense. But the social enterprise changes that are happening in Uganda are examples of people taking control for themselves. They are changing their own world for the better by creating a change in ownership and a change in the market for boda. And in time, East Timor will hopefully do the same. Sure, the fishing people of Alaska have been dealt a bad hand by a change in legislation, but they will find a way out of it or possibly re-train themselves to do something different."

"But why should they have to?" asked Frank. "The US government has massively affected their livelihoods."

"Maybe they had to be cruel to be kind? If the fishermen were depleting fish stocks by overfishing, then the government has applied a form of market correction to ensure their industry is sustainable in the future."

"It's like the problem with steel over here, Frank," said Elliot. "The Chinese are selling off their own steel to us at a cut down price and it's killing our industry. So the people in the steel industry will have to retrain and find new work."

"But why should they?" replied Frank. "The government should protect their jobs by placing a subsidy on British steel so they are price competitive. We give up our primary and secondary industries too easily. There are millions of working families who depend on them. If we close down those industries, we create an added demand for jobs in the tertiary sector that don't exist. It happened with mining in the 80s and those communities took two decades to get back on their feet."

"Yes, I agree," said Alex.

"We actually agree on something? I'll mark it in my diary as a day to remember!" said Frank sarcastically.

"There has to be a first time for everything, right? No, you are totally right. I think with coal mining, the problem was that cheaper forms of energy were emerging. But with steel, I don't see a viable alternative. We still need it in whatever form it takes. So we should protect the manufacture of it in our own country. But the buyers of steel are not just the government and businesses have no ethical obligation to buy British made steel, so they would have to be induced by subsidy or other form of incentive. So it will cost the government a fortune."

"Or, they just figure out a way to produce it more cost effectively?" asked Natasha.

"I think they would argue that they already are. It's just that China is able to produce it cheaper by paying lower wages. Plus, they are sitting on a mountain of the stuff."

"Anyway, who's for another drink?" asked Elliot. "Let's see if we can deplete some of the alcohol stocks of this pub some more!"

"I'd better be going," I said.

Alex looked a little sad. "I'd better make a move, too," he said.

"But who will Frank have to argue with if you leave, Alex?" asked Natasha.

"Well, I'm sure one of you will step into the breach."

We started putting on our coats and said our goodbyes.

"Now I insist you let me walk you home this time," said Alex outside. "It's dark."

"Well if you insist, then how can I refuse?" I replied.

As we walked, Alex told me about a few of his previous battles with Frank. It was clear they didn't see eye to eye on just about anything, which made their agreement on steel subsidy quite an event.

We reached my house. "Well, thanks for inviting me tonight. I really enjoyed it a lot," I said honestly.

"You are very welcome," said Alex. As he said it, he leant over to kiss my cheek.

"Is that the best you can do?" I asked. He smiled and returned to kiss me on the lips, which lasted a little longer than the kiss on the cheek.

"That was much better," I said. "Good night." He grabbed my hand just as I was about to turn and pulled me in, one more time.

What you've covered:

Theme	Amplification
Change	The significance of change within both business and global economies
Change	Distinguish between internal and external change
Change	Kurt Lewin's 'Three Step Model of Change'
Change	The distinction between planned and unplanned change
Political	How government decisions affect industry

Memory hook: Angry Frank

The Angry Frank argument reinforces the significance of change in business. Some changes are internal; others are imposed upon them externally. Some changes are planned; others are unplanned. It is how businesses react to and manage change that, for the most part, decides the outcome.

So, key points to remember:

1. Lewin's three steps are:
    a. unfreezing – ending the bad behaviours
    b. change – making the necessary changes
    c. refreezing – embedding the new approach to make it permanent.

2. Subsidies can be applied to certain industries by governments to provide support through difficult times. Governments will do this if those industries are of great importance to their country or its strategy. In the 1980s, the UK government decided the coal industry was no longer important and chose not to subsidise it.

Now ask yourself:

1. Can you give some examples of products or sectors that have experienced significant change?

Now ask yourself (suggested answers):

1. **Can you give some examples of products or sectors that have experienced significant change?**

   ▪ Computer and entertainment storage media has undergone extensive change. Videotape and floppy disk were both replaced by DVD/CD, which itself is now being pushed out through cloud storage and downloads.

   ▪ Book publishing has changed significantly through the evolution of self-publishing. The barriers to publishing have been removed and traditional publishers are facing threat from self-publishers via Amazon.

   ▪ The travel industry has experienced change from a historical dependency on travel agents to travel websites and online budget airlines.

I joined my Mum in the conservatory the next morning. She was studying some kind of leaflet.

"Good morning," I said, placing my coffee down on the glass part of the table.

"Coaster, please." My Mum was very particular about where cups were placed.

"What are you reading?" I asked.

"Just more work stuff." Mum gave a heavy sigh. "It's an update I was sent by the works council."

"What's the works council?"

"It's basically a committee of staff from the council who have been elected to represent us."

"I thought that was the job of the trade union?"

"It is. But the trade union operates nationally. At that level, it's hard to represent local issues. So the works council is specific to us."

"So, what's the update about?"

"Well apparently, the level of job cuts has prompted a number of people to demand strike action. So this leaflet is updating us on what they feel is the best way forward."

"And what are they proposing?"

"A lot of it is challenging the council on how they are acting. So according to something called ICE, which stands for…" Mum paused to read the leaflet, "…the European Union's Information and Consultation of Employees regulation, they have failed to communicate with us in an effective and constructive way. And since they are planning over twenty redundancies, they should have consulted with them by now. But it seems like they haven't."

"So does that help your case?"

"Well, it then goes on to say they are trying to secure a 'no-strike deal' in return for the council agreeing to reduce its proposed number of job cuts. So they want the number of job cuts to be halved."

"Ooh that sounds promising. That could mean your job stays!"

"It could do. Although they're also in preliminary discussions with ACAS to arrange conciliation if they don't get the job cuts they've asked for."

"I've heard of ACAS."

"Yes, they helped advise Sally with her employment tribunal over Crazy Daisy. So they basically act independently to resolve disputes between workers and employers."

"And what does conciliation mean?"

"It kind of means helping to find a solution when two people disagree. So I have spent most of the last ten years doing conciliation between you and your brother!"

"You mean listening and then deciding I was right all along."

"Not always. You've had your moments over the years, too."

"Yeah, usually because he used to lie through his teeth to make me look bad. Anyway, I don't think it was conciliation that you did. More like the judge, jury and executioner."

"Hey, that's not fair! I always tried to make you resolve your differences. It's just that most of the time you would never agree, so I had to act as arbitrator."

"Meaning?"

"Meaning I had the final say over what the outcome was."

"My point exactly. Judge, jury and executioner."

"You make me sound like something out of the Spanish Inquisition, Lu! Anyway, how did it go last night? You were late back?"

"Yes, they went to the pub afterwards. I didn't want to knock on your door when I got back."

"I was awake until I heard you come in. Then I turned in for an early night."

"That was early. I was back by half nine!"

"I know, but I was up early this morning on the treadmill." Mum had bought a treadmill to get fit, which we kept in the garage. "I managed five miles."

"Oh, well done. I don't think I could manage that."

"Well, it's there when you need it. Anyway I'm going to put the pots in the dishwasher before setting off. Can I take that cup?"

"It's OK, I might have a re-fill as classes don't start until eleven."

"Oh to be young again!" said Mum as she left the room.

I was glad she didn't grill me about Alex, as my face would have given it all away.

What you've covered:

Theme	Amplification
Employer/employee relationships	The difference between a trade union and a works council
Employer/employee Relationships	The role of ACAS in resolving disputes
Employer/employee Relationships	The difference between conciliation and arbitration

Memory hook: Judge, jury and executioner

'Judge, jury and executioner' is used here to mean arbitration. The act of conciliation is to get two parties in dispute to resolve their differences. The role of arbitration is similar, but the arbitrator has the final decision and both parties must be bound by that decision.

So, key points to remember:

1. A works council is a forum within an organisation that's run by employees to discuss issues. A trade union operates across a whole industry and will have individual members within a local organisation in the role of 'union rep'.
2. ACAS stands for Advisory, Conciliation and Arbitration Service. The UK Government set it up in 1975.

Now ask yourself:

1. What are the major costs of industrial disputes to both employers and its workers?
2. Are trade unions just there to serve 'shop floor' workers or do they also serve management?

Now ask yourself (suggested answers):

1. **What are the major costs of industrial disputes to both employers and its workers?**

    Employer:
    - The employer is likely to be affected by a drop in morale of its staff and consequently reduced productivity.
    - If the dispute means that work doesn't get done, then the business may lose revenue and/or contracts with disgruntled customers.
    - The employer is likely to receive negative publicity from a dispute, which may damage external relationships with stakeholders.

    Workers:
    - When workers take strike action, they typically won't receive pay for the days they strike.
    - Disputes could cause tension between those in favour and those against the strike action.
    - Workers may feel that taking a negative stance on the dispute could affect their relationship with management in the present and the future.

2. **Are trade unions just there to serve 'shop floor' workers or do they also serve management?**

    Trade unions serve all of their members, regardless of their status. However, since it is management that are principally being challenged by the trade unions on the decisions they have made, it is usual to assume that the trade unions are against management. Also, management are less likely to belong to the union.

CHAPTER 19

LoveVentriloquism.com

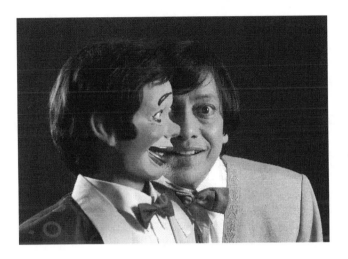

My next meeting with Alex was our first proper 'date'. He had invited me to a comedy club with a few of his friends.

The first guy I spoke to was called Ashley, but everyone knew him as Ash. He had known Alex since their first week of university and they had stayed close friends ever since. Alex left us to talk while he went to the bar.

"So, I've heard a lot about you!" he said. "Nice to put a face to the name." I shook his hand awkwardly.

"I'm not sure if I should be worried by that or not?" I asked.

"Well, given his usual taste in girlfriends, we were all expecting the worst. But I have to say, first impressions suggest he may just have turned the corner."

"Right, well now I'm definitely worried," I said. "Has he had many girlfriends?" I immediately wished I hadn't asked that, but sometimes the questions in my mind come straight out without passing through the etiquette filter.

"Nah, he scares most of them off within the first five minutes of opening his mouth."

"Whereas you are a total sex God?" I said immediately, feeling a surge of defensiveness towards Alex.

"You've noticed!" replied Ash.

"I'm sure in some parallel universe, you would be considered that." This wasn't quite how I intended my first introduction with one of his friends to go.

He looked slightly pained but tried hard to conceal it. "Nice come back! Maybe you should get up on stage for the open mic session tonight?"

"It will take a lot of vodkas to persuade me to do that."

"Well, I'm sure getting you to down multiple vodkas is part of his plan for the night." The conversation was getting totally awkward, so I was relieved when Alex returned with our drinks.

"I got you a double, as they were on offer," he said, handing me a tall glass.

Ash laughed and as I looked at him, he winked jubilantly.

"Have I missed something?" asked Alex.

"I was just telling Lucinda that it should be a good night," said Ash slyly. I had taken an immediate dislike to him, which could be a problem with him being Alex's best friend.

Fortunately we were soon joined by more of his friends, one of whom was female. She was called Jocelyn, but everyone called her JC. She was the girlfriend of another guy there, called Mike. The three of us chatted for quite a while until the MC took to the stage.

The first comedian was pretty good, although his entire act was one-liners, which got a bit tiring after a while. He suffered a bit of heckling when his one-liners stopped being that funny. It brought home to me the bravery of these people who were doing this for a living.

In the break, I got chatting to the last member of the group that I hadn't properly spoken to. His name was Will and he had come on his own. Alex had told me in advance that he had recently split with his girlfriend and was a bit sad about it. I decided not to probe, as he didn't look that sad, so I didn't want to spoil his evening. It turned out that he was planning to launch a business of his own, so we had something in common.

"My plan is to launch a website promoting stand-up comedy," he said. "Which is why I keep dragging this lot here."

"That's interesting," I said, honestly. "But hasn't that already been done?"

"Sort of, but not very well. There's quite a few websites promoting comedy clubs. So the main one nationally is *chortle*. Then established comedians like Jason Manford have their own websites too. And of course, Google Places does it regionally."

"So, how will yours be different?" I asked.

"OK, the plan is to create a platform so that wannabe comedians can pitch their act. You kind of have people doing it on YouTube already, but I want to bring it all into one place and enable people to vote on each act they watch."

"Oh wow, I get it," I said. "That sounds like a great idea!"

"Well, I hope so. It will be aimed mainly at mobile devices. And the plan is to get people to join through their social media accounts. Then we send them daily updates of new acts that have been posted."

"Do you plan to make money from it?"

"Urm, hopefully yeah," he said. I could tell he felt this was a silly question. "But it will take time to build up, so I'm mainly doing it in my spare time."

I still couldn't see how he would make money and decided to be bold and ask. "So, how will it make money?"

"Well, at the same time as getting new acts to perform, I'm creating a database of comedy venues. So if the venue sees an act they like, they can book them directly from the site and we receive commission. Plus, every week we'll send all the venues a list of the top ten ranked acts, so they can choose the pick of the litter, as it were."

"OK. I guess there's quite a lot of comedy clubs to tap into?"

"I've estimated 2,750 over the whole of the UK. I've got about six hundred in the database already." He looked quite proud of this. "That's proper ones that pay for the acts. So my target for the first two years is to do regular business with five percent of them, which would be 137 clubs." He kept looking up at the ceiling as he tried to recall what he obviously had written down somewhere. "Then, I've estimated the average commission I could make per venue to be ten quid a week. This would make my weekly revenue around £1,375. At that point, I would give up the day job."

"Wow, it sounds like you've got it all planned out," I said, feeling a little concerned I hadn't done these kind of calculations. "So, when will it be up and running?"

"The website is in maintenance mode right now and should be launched in a couple of months. I'm currently scouring YouTube for some acts that might want to upload their content so I have something to work with initially. Plus, I've emailed hundreds of venues to tell them it's coming."

"Sounds like a lot of work!"

"Yeah, the thing I'm a bit scared of is tipping someone off on what I'm planning so they get in before me. I reckon there's a real gap in the market."

I nodded. "I know that feeling! That was exactly how I felt when I first thought of my idea: 'how do I stop people stealing it?'"

"Oh cool, so you are starting a business too. What's yours?" I shared my idea with Will until the comedy show got back under way, relieved to find him much easier to talk to than Ash!

The final act was great and we were all in stitches. The boys replayed all the best bits as we walked over to the nearest pub. I was hoping to talk to Alex as I hadn't spent much time with him all night, but Will came over, which I didn't mind too much.

"I've been thinking about your USP," he said casually, although he looked quite serious.

"Is that unique selling point?" I asked. I was beginning to pick up some of the business terms Alex used.

"That's the one. Well, I know this probably doesn't help you because you make the cover, not the duvet itself." Will was slurring his words slightly and had that drunken look on his face. Ever since Ash's comment about downing vodkas, I'd been careful to pace myself and kept refusing offers for refills, so I was probably the most sober of them all. "One of the problems I have making the bed is figuring out which way the duvet is meant to go. I mean, it's meant to be rectangular right? But it's really hard to see which is the long side and which is the short one."

"I agree totally! You have a good point," I said.

"I definitely do. So if there was some way to colour code the sides, so you can see which way around it goes, that would really help sell it."

As he'd already pointed out that I wasn't planning on making the duvets, I just nodded my agreement. "I guess your USP is the fact that everyday people can upload their comedy sketches?"

"That's right." Will wobbled slightly as he spoke and I was slightly worried he was going to go flying. "Nobody does it right now. Plus, to differentiate it even further, I want to create a 'Love' brand and have a product portfolio of different categories for different acts. The current trend is more performance variety stuff thanks to TV programmes like 'Britain's Got Talent'. So 'Love Stand-up'; 'Love Magic'; 'Love Dance'. I need to find another word for ventriloquism because it's not very catchy is it?"

"Plus, I think you might find the market for ventriloquists a bit more limited than comedians," I replied.

As we arrived at the pub, Alex came over and put his arms around both of us. "At last, I've managed to get away from that rabble," he said jokingly. "So, you two been sharing tips?" He winked at me as he spoke.

"We've been talking USPs to be precise," I said, hoping that Alex would sense my need for rescuing. Not that Will wasn't nice; the conversation was just getting a little dry.

"Well, let's agree not to talk shop for the rest of the night."

"You've found a good one here," said Will, looking over at me. "Makes a change." I was beginning to get really interested in Alex's psycho exes."

"I can't wait to meet some of your previous girlfriends," I said.

"Don't go there," replied Alex tersely. "Right, my round. What are we having?"

We stayed for a couple more rounds, until finally Alex walked me home. I was feeling pretty juiced by this time.

I remember we held hands all the way. At a lull in the drunken conversation, I brought up the subject of Ash's comments.

"So, what's the story with your bonkers ex-girlfriends?"

He laughed. "Let me guess. Ash has been giving me some grief?"

"Just a bit. It sounds like I'm the normal one in a pack full of crazies."

"I admit one or two were a bit left of centre."

"They're not about to jump out of one of these bushes are they?"

"No chance. They're well and truly off the scene."

"How can you be so sure?"

"Well if you must know, I've buried them all under the patio."

I squeezed his hand tightly. "Yeah, I thought 'axe murderer' the first minute I set eyes on you!"

"Nah, the axe is too old school. I'm a strictly chainsaw massacre man."

"You'd better be kidding."

"Well, you'll just have to stick around and find out. As for my ex's, they're all history, I promise."

We arrived back at the house. This time we moved into the shadows and enjoyed a more passionate kiss.

What you've covered:

Theme	Amplification
Markets	How to calculate market size and market share
Markets	How changing trends in the market affect the way a business sells itself
The Marketing Mix	The meaning of unique selling point (USP)
The Marketing Mix	The thinking behind brand differentiation and product portfolio

Memory hook: LoveVentriloquism.com

Will's need for 'Love Ventriloquism' is a mental cue for what is meant by a product portfolio. Consider how he uses this portfolio to differentiate his business idea from others by offering more variety than just comedy. Identifying a changing trend in the market influenced this for him.

So, key points to remember:

1. A unique selling point (USP) is a single idea or concept that differentiates a business from its competitors in the same market.
2. A brand encompasses everything a company wants their potential customers to think about when they consider buying one of their products. So it includes the name and logo, but also their reputation and what they stand for.
3. A product portfolio is a group of products sold within one business.
4. Market size represents the total potential business that can be conducted within an industry. It would typically be calculated on a monetary basis.
5. Market share is the percentage of the total market size that a company controls. So if, in a market size of £10 million, a company has a turnover of £1 million, they hold a 10% market share.

Now ask yourself:

1. Consider the following three companies: Apple, Ben & Jerry's and HSBC. How would you describe their brand identities and what are their product portfolios?

Now ask yourself (suggested answers):

1. **Consider the following three companies: Apple, Ben & Jerry's and HSBC. How would you describe their brand identities and what are their product portfolios?**

Apple
Their brand identity is focused on quality, innovation and aesthetics. The portfolio includes hardware – iPhone, iPad, iPod etc., but also the purchase of apps and other peripherals such as headphones.

Ben & Jerry's
Their brand identity is focused on a three way mission of product excellence, sustainability and social gain. They also try to project an element of fun through their packaging, website and other marketing channels.
Their portfolio is mainly ice cream, however they also innovate in partnering with other organisations. For example, this year they work with a social enterprise called Luminary to provide the 'wich – a combo of cookie and ice cream.

HSBC
Their brand identity is about financial security and generating wealth. Their portfolio is a cross-section of financial services including bank accounts, mortgages and loans, credit cards, insurance and investments. They also service both business and individuals.

CHAPTER 20

Second Life

On Sunday, I was to meet Alex at a local coffee shop at a ridiculously early hour. Well, 8am is pretty early for a Sunday! He had a surprise morning for me and was going to explain over coffee. He was waiting outside as I was predictably ten minutes late and we kissed and hugged.

"We need to sort your punctuality out if you are going to be a high-flying business woman, Ms Lopez-Lawson!"

"And just who has a business meeting at 8am on a Sunday morning, might I ask? Mr Chapman!" I nudged him teasingly in the ribs. "Anyway, it's a ladies prerogative to be late. Although it is nice that you are on time and wait for me outside."

"Give it a couple of months and I'll be fifteen minutes late myself!"

"Ahem, it's ten minutes. And no, please carry on being your lovely self. Right, come on I'll buy the coffee seeing as I'm TEN minutes late."

We drank our vanilla lattes and Alex told me what he had in store for us. We were going to help out with a local social enterprise he knew called

Second Life. Someone he had come to know through the university called Philippa had set it up.

"So, Second Life is aimed at children aged 11-16 who are going through tough times. They have all kinds of kids on board. Some are carers for sick parents. Some are being bullied. Quite a few have minor mental disorders such as ADHD and autism."

"OK. How do they get involved in Second Life?"

"Well, they need to get a referral from either their GP or a social worker. That's important, as otherwise Philippa can't claim the funding."

"So she gets paid to do this?"

"Oh yes, it's run very much like a business. Most social enterprises are."

"Who pays her for looking after the kids?"

"For Second Life, she responded to a tender." Alex could see I was looking confused. "So basically, the local authority put out a brief for a piece of work they want doing. That's called a tender. People like Philippa apply to do the work. Whichever enterprise is successful gets the job. Philippa was successful. I think it's a three year project and she's about six months in, so she will get paid for doing this for the next two and a half years."

"Without sounding mean, why would the local authority pay someone to do this? Isn't it their job?"

"Ah, well that's a good question!" He took a quick slurp of coffee as I could tell he was dying to explain it. "Years ago, they probably would. Or more likely, it wouldn't have been done at all, as back then we weren't very good at recognising and responding to social issues. But nowadays, society is more aware of its needs. So there is more demand for these types of activities. The problem is that the public sector, which is basically government plus local authorities and emergency services, are not set up to do a lot of this kind of thing. Social enterprises have emerged to fill the gap between what the public sector can't do and the private sector won't do."

"Yeah, my Mum's kind of experiencing this herself right now. She's in the public sector, but her job is at risk and the work might get shipped out to the third sector."

"That's tough," replied Alex.

"Anyway, that's another story," I cut in quickly. "So when you say 'years ago', how long do you mean?"

"Well even back in the 1980s, there wasn't much in the way of support for social problems. So people would pretty much sort things out within families or just use what was available like youth clubs and stuff. Thirty or so years ago, it was far less common for both parents to work and so challenged kids would spend most of their time with their Mums. Obviously I don't know this from my own experience because I wasn't even born then – see, told you I'm not that old!"

"Yeah right, Grandad! Seriously, my Aunt Kath was explaining all this to me last week. I had no idea so many different ways of running a business existed."

"A good example is mutual businesses, such as co-operatives. The Co-operative Group is one example, but there are others like farmers co-operatives. The members of the mutual run them. Then you have Building Societies, which are an alternative to high street banks. They are an example of a social enterprise because they pass their profits onto their members through better interest rates. The people who invest their money with them have a share of the enterprise."

"Isn't John Lewis owned by its employees? Is that a co-operative?"

"Strictly speaking it's a partnership. But you're right, it has elements of co-operative working since the workers own a share of the company. This helps incentivise them to perform well because they earn a bonus at the end of the year based on how much profit the company makes."

"So, is this her full-time job?"

"Philippa? No, not at all. She's 100 mph, as you'll see when you meet her. Her actual enterprise is called Fresh Start, but what she does with these kids is under the Second Life project. She has other projects on the go as well, but they are all in this area of social support. You can imagine it like any other business. But Fresh Start has what's called a Board of Trustees. They are people who Philippa has recruited to oversee the work she does. They don't get paid though. So, she is accountable to them, which means she can't go charging herself £100k or something."

"But it's her business, so shouldn't she be able to do what she likes?"

"No, not as a social enterprise. Even though she created it, she still has an obligation to 'do the right thing'. The Trustees are there to ensure she does that. And it really helps her actually because her Trustees have lots of experience, so they are basically providing her with free advice. Plus, when she applies for these tenders, the fact that her Trustees are so well respected improves her chances of winning."

"How old is she?"

"Twenty one."

"Oh my God, I can't believe she's doing all this at such a young age!"

"You're doing something just as impressive at an even younger age! Although she started when she was about your age, which is why I want you to meet her – I think you will hit it off. Come on, we'd better go," he said, taking a final slurp of coffee. "Ooh, one thing I must warn you. Don't, whatever you do, refer to them as problem children or children with issues, or anything like that. She gets really cross about that as she is incredibly defensive of her kids."

"Oh my God, now I'm scared. I have a habit of putting my foot in it! What if I say the wrong thing and she hates me?!"

"Don't worry, you'll be fine."

"So what should I call them?"

"She calls them her team, but I think she is fine with just 'kids'."

"Kids it is then."

What you've covered:

Theme	Amplification
Business Structure	The difference between the role of the not-for-profit sector and the public and private sectors
Business Structure	Social enterprises and co-operatives as examples of the not-for-profit sector
Business Structure	The role of the Board of Trustees in a social enterprise
PESTLE: Social	The impact of social factors on business and the economy

Memory hook: Second Life

Philippa created the Second Life project to support disadvantaged children and their families. This is another example of a social enterprise. Just like Silver Surfers, it operates as any other business would, except any profit (referred to as surplus) must be re-invested back into the enterprise.

So, key points to remember:

1. The not-for-profit sector comprises a number of structures: charities, social enterprises, co-operatives and societies.
2. Social issues often create enterprise opportunities, particularly as the role of the public sector is shrinking.

Now ask yourself:

1. The Big Issue is a well-known example of a social enterprise in the UK. What do you know about why and how it is in operation?
2. Can you give one example each of: a charity, a not-for-profit business and a mutual business?

Now ask yourself (suggested answers):

1. **The Big Issue is a well-known example of a social enterprise in the UK. What do you know about why and how it is in operation?**

    Two guys who wanted to address the problem of homelessness in London founded the Big Issue back in 1991. They believed that helping people to help themselves was the best way to combat homelessness. Vendors of The Big Issue magazine are homeless people who receive a share of every magazine they sell. The enterprise values their impact in terms of 'positive outcomes', such as getting someone out of homelessness or earning a job. They achieved 8,450 positive outcomes in 2015.

2. **Can you give one example each of: a charity, a not-for-profit business and a mutual business?**

    Most well known charities are created to support vulnerable groups. Examples include: Barnardo's (children), Help the Aged (older people), RSPCA (animals) and Help for Heroes (former military personnel).

    UNICEF is possibly the highest profile not-for-profit organisation globally. However, many exist around the UK.

    As of 2015, there were 6,796 mutuals in the UK. The biggest two by far are the John Lewis Partnership and The Co-operative Group.

CHAPTER 21

The Horse and Water

Over the next few days my mind was buzzing with two things. Firstly, how totally amazing Alex was and secondly how utterly awesome Philippa was!

The way she interacted with her kids was unbelievable. Even though she owned the company, she was hands-on with everything, from making the drinks in the kitchen to running all the games they played. The kids had such a great time that I could see how she got so much out of her day.

Although she was too busy to talk during the session, she stayed behind once the kids had gone home and chatted for ages. She was really friendly and helpful, telling me all about the struggles she encountered setting the enterprise up in the first place. She preferred not to refer to it as a business and explained why they were her 'team'. She believes passionately that disadvantaged children should be offered the trust of being treated as equals, until a point where they relinquish that trust. That way, they will recover the confidence and self-esteem lost through whatever problems they are dealing with elsewhere in their lives.

So days later, when Uncle Steve was driving me to see a guy called Ricardo, I couldn't stop telling him all about my experience.

"It sounds great Lulu, but now I need to get a word in edge ways to prepare you for meeting Ric."

"Sure, fill me in boss," I said sarcastically.

"So, Ric owns a pub restaurant called 'The Horse and Water'. I've told you about him before."

"Yeah, he's the guy that turned his restaurant around through crowdfunding."

"Yes, so most of what he received was actually services, rather than money. It's kind of a modern day form of bartering."

"Bartering being?" I asked.

"Bartering being when the transactions are in the form of services, rather than cash. So I paint your bedroom, in exchange for you helping me with my annual accounts."

"I'm not letting you anywhere near by bedroom walls! You're hopeless at DIY."

"Thanks. And there's no chance you're being let loose on my accounts." We arrived at The Horse and Water. "Anyway, we're here now, so you can hear it from the horse's mouth!"

"Hilarious."

I was introduced to Ric. He was taking a break from duties, so we were able to sit down and have a drink with him. He began to tell me his story.

"We took over the pub about eight years ago. The first year was alright, but once the smoking ban came into force, we saw a steady decline in turnover. The bulk of our trade is locals from the town and surrounding villages.

"The big problem came when our main competitor in the town changed hands. What happened was a large chain of budget restaurants took it over. With their name and advertising power, they took more of our food business away. Plus, the pub and restaurant sector was really struggling at the time anyway. The recession meant that people's real incomes had gone down."

"Inflation means that the cost of buying stuff basically goes up each year," added Uncle Steve. "It's usually about two percent per year. So if people's wages don't rise in line with inflation, then people have the same amount of money coming in, but the cost of buying things has gone up. In a recession, most people don't receive a pay rise. Consequently, they have to cut back on what they spend."

"And when people tighten their belts, guess what one of the first things they cut back on is? Eating out. Which is why our industry is so sensitive to the economy."

"I get it," I said.

"So one evening, myself and Laura went to experience the competition for ourselves." Laura was his wife. "It was typical of most of these chains; ready meals bought in and just heated up in microwaves. What it made us do was re-evaluate what we were doing. At one stage we had considered packing it all in. But that evening actually focused our minds to do something positive about it.

"All of our food has always been home cooked, but up until that point, we agreed it had been largely uninspiring. So two things needed to change. Firstly: a more exciting menu. And secondly, we wanted to open up the kitchen area from the restaurant so we could show everyone what they were buying. No microwaves and a spotlessly clean kitchen.

"The only problem was, we were flat broke. Those two years had hit us hard and we lost money badly. So, when we saw the bank to discuss a loan for the changes, we got turned down. They said we were too high a risk. Around that time of course, the country was emerging from the recession and banks weren't lending any money. That really didn't help matters.

"We only needed £5,000, which was a small amount. But still, they wouldn't lend due to our poor trading history. One of the jobs we had decided to do was knock through into an unused junk room to create space for an extra three tables. The bank asked why we needed more tables when we were clearly under utilised. It just shows they didn't understand our business because there were periods in the week when we were operating at full capacity and had to turn people away. The problem was the days when we were quiet.

"We had no reserves or family to fall back on. Then, Laura read an article about crowdfunding in a magazine and we decided to give it a go. So we created a page on one of the crowdfunding websites and put lots of posters up in the pub and around the village.

"The response was overwhelming and within three weeks we had raised the money. In fact, one of our locals was a builder and he even agreed to do all the labour for free, in exchange for some free meals. So within two months, it had all been renovated and this is the result."

I looked around the room as he spoke and sure enough, everything was open plan. It was a really nice looking restaurant.

"But you went even further than that, didn't you?" asked Uncle Steve.

"Yes, then we had the real brainwave. We realised that our USP was good, home cooked food, compared to the junk they served down the road. So we visited a local farm shop to enquire about becoming a supplier. The farm shop has an excellent reputation so Laura, being the ace negotiator she is, ensured that as part of the deal we got to use their brand and logo on our menus and posters.

"This turned out to be a masterstroke. The cost of their produce was quite a bit higher than we had paid before, which meant our margins were lower. But as part of the new look menu, we were providing better quality in lower quantities. This meant our prices didn't change significantly. Even though we were making slightly less profit per cover, we were getting so many more customers that it didn't matter.

"The last thing we did was to reinvent the place on the less busy nights. So we created themed nights and did more work with the local community to get them to use us. This was all about capacity utilisation.

In other words, we needed to maximise our usage of every table in the restaurant area as much as possible."

"What sort of things did you do with the community?" I asked, thinking about Philippa and Second Life.

"Well, there are lots of community clubs and societies, so we gave them a great deal to hold their meetings here. Stuff like that. Within eighteen months, we went from losing over £1,000 a month, to making a profit of around £2,000 each month. We took so much trade from the big chain that they closed down, which was fantastic!"

"What you've done is amazing," I said honestly. "But how did you know it was going to work?"

Ric paused for a few seconds. "I think like everything in business, it was a bit of a gamble. But the greatest change I made personally was to understand the financials better. So, when we were haemorrhaging money left, right and centre, I didn't really understand what was going wrong.

"The most important thing I've learnt is the importance of financial *contribution*. Are you familiar with that term Lucinda?" I shook my head. "Contribution is what's left when you subtract your variable costs from your revenue. So, suppose you both ate with us tonight and let's say your bill came to £30. It might have cost us £20 to provide your two meals and drinks. That would be the cost of the ingredients, the electricity needed for cooking, the chef to prepare it and the waiting staff to serve it. Those are my *variable costs*. They're variable because if I don't open the door, I don't have to pay those costs. That would give me a contribution of £10, which I then use to cover my *fixed costs*. So, my fixed costs need to be paid each month, irrespective of whether I open the door or not. That would include the rent on the building, rates and business insurance, plus our own living costs. And if we have anything left over after those deductions, then we've made a profit.

"Now before, I had no idea what our contribution was. But now, we have daily, weekly and monthly targets based on our contribution, because we know what our fixed costs are going to be. This means all our meals are priced to ensure we generate roughly the same contribution from every customer.

"The other thing we do is look at *break-even* in a different way. Before, we thought about break-even from the perspective of money. Now, because we manage our contribution better, we think of break-even as the number of customers each day. So on our off-peak days, which are basically Monday to Thursday, we need to hit around twenty covers per day. In restaurant speak, a cover is basically a customer. On the peak days, because we employ more staff, we need to hit around thirty five covers."

I thought back to his crowdfunding initiative. "What about the people who invested in you? Didn't providing all those free meals hit your profits?"

"That's a good point. We were quite clever there. Or at least, Laura was! When we gave away the meal packages in return for investment, we made sure they were only redeemable on a Monday to Thursday. So it didn't hit our peak trade. Plus, the fact we had more people in our restaurant through the week actually helped us. You'd be surprised at what a full car park does for business! If people see a car park is full, there is an immediate perception that it must be good."

Ric's wife Laura came over to join us. She definitely looked like the brains of the outfit. As she had to go to an appointment, Ric was needed to take over, so I thanked him for his time and we headed back home.

"We need to do some projections for your business now I think, Lulu," said Uncle Steve in the car.

"Definitely! I need to make sure I get a handle on this contribution thing. It sounds like a big deal."

What you've covered:

Theme	Amplification
Measures of finance	The concepts of inflation and real income
Sources of finance	The benefits and nature of crowdfunding
Revenue and costs	Variable and fixed costs and why they matter
Revenue and costs	Calculating contribution and interpreting its relevance to the calculation of break-even
Productivity	The concept of capacity utilisation

Memory hook: The Horse and Water

The Horse and Water was a struggling business that reinvented itself. It achieved this by using an innovative source of finance (crowdfunding) and better understanding the calculation of contribution.

So, key points to remember:

1. Crowdfunding invites the public to invest small amounts into a business in return for some form of payback in the future.
2. Contribution is the difference between revenue and variable costs.
3. Profit is calculated by subtracting the fixed costs from the contribution. So one measure of break-even is when the contribution exactly equals the fixed costs.
4. Real income is equal to income that has been adjusted for the rise/fall in inflation. Suppose a person earns £2,100 each month and their overall monthly expenditure is £2,000 per month. They therefore have £100 in surplus each month. If in 12 months time, their total expenditure has risen by 5%, then their outgoings will now be £2,000 x 5% = £2,100. But if their income doesn't go up at all in that time, they now have no money left over each month. So their income hasn't changed, but their real income has reduced by £100.

Now ask yourself:

1. Why are real income and inflation relevant to pound shops?
2. What is one of the key limiting factors for supermarkets and what options are open to them when challenged by new competitors entering the market, such as Aldi and Lidl?

Now ask yourself (suggested answers):

1. **Why is real income and inflation relevant to pound shops?**
   Real income takes account of inflation and so is a more accurate reflection of the disposable income available to households. When disposable income is low, pound shops are likely to perform well because people look to spend less. However, challenging economic times also make it harder for business-to-business suppliers to find customers for their products. This means that pound shops are able to negotiate better deals for their surplus stock.

   Inflation has a direct relationship with currency value. So when inflation in a country is high, pounds shops will seek to buy much of their stock overseas.

2. **What is one of the key limiting factors for supermarkets and what options are open to them when challenged by new competitors entering the market, such as Aldi and Lidl?**
   The problem for supermarkets is there is a limit to how much people need to spend on groceries. So unless the population size increases, the value of the market is capped to a large extent. This means most supermarkets are competing on market share within the market. When new competitors such as Aldi and Lidl enter the market, they take some of that share. So existing mainstream supermarkets must adapt their strategy to entice people to shop with them. Strategies might include:

   - Widening their product range so they sell more goods that new competitors don't, e.g. mobile phones, insurance etc.
   - Re-thinking their distribution and sales channels, e.g. selling more products online and focusing on home delivery.
   - Creating a niche, for example taking their product range more upmarket. However, companies such as Waitrose and M&S already dominate the premium market. It's also not easy to change customer perception of a brand identity.
   - Incentivising customers with offers (e.g. discounted petrol) and loyalty cards.
   - Managing costs better by reducing the size of the workforce or finding efficiencies within their supply chain.
   - Improving margins by squeezing their suppliers on price.

CHAPTER 22

Stitch on-time

The following day, Aunt Kath and I set off to meet a friend of Brita who was running a sewing business called 'Stitch-on-time' from her own home. Her name was Kate. She had two dogs called Jasper and Barry who were barking like mad when we rang the doorbell. After sorting out the dogs, Kate opened the door. She was really pretty and looked to be in her mid-thirties.

"Hi," she beamed, "is it Katherine and Lucinda?"

"Yes, but please call me Kath," said my Aunt.

"Come on in. I've never liked Katherine either. It reminds me of being told off by my Mum as a child! Excuse the dogs; I've put them in the conservatory. They're not nearly as scary as they sound."

She took us into her lounge and went off to make us some coffee. As the dogs were still barking, she asked if we'd mind just saying hello to them, as then they would quieten down. Jasper and Barry were two adorable Bichon Frises! They had long, lanky hair that covered their eyes and their tails kept hitting the furniture as they were wagging so much.

"So, the darker haired one is Jasper. And this is Barry," said Kate, giving Barry a big pat on his back leg. I laughed when she said his name.

"If you don't mind me asking, why is he called Barry?"

"Oh, don't even go there!" said Kate. "When we got them, we agreed that I could name one and he, that's my partner Des, would name the other. So I came up with Jasper and Des said that was way too posh, so he balanced it out with a more 'down to earth' name. Barry! I could have killed him. It's so embarrassing calling him in the park on walks. I've got used to it now, but in the first few months, I wouldn't let him off the lead for fear of having to shout his name. And then when I did, I used to whisper it so that nobody would hear me. The problem was that Barry couldn't hear me either, so he would never come back!"

We all laughed. Kate put the dogs back in the conservatory and we sat down with the coffees. I told her all about my idea and she explained to me what she did.

"Des is away quite a bit on business trips, so it's often just me and the dogs. I used to work in a solicitor's office, but I got a bit bored of it, so I decided to do what I was passionate about. I've always loved sewing. So we converted our garage and I started up the business. It's been going so well that I'm working more hours now than I was in the office."

"I like the name!" I said.

"Stitch on-time? Thanks. That was his idea, too. A bit better than Barry!"

"So, if you're really busy, I guess you won't have much time available to help me with mine?" I asked nervously.

"Well, work comes and goes, so provided it's planned, it should be fine. A lot of the work I do is prototyping for large apparel clients. But I also make quite a lot of wedding dresses. You'd be amazed how many women want a wedding dress making in a week. 'Shotgun weddings' Des calls them! Because our USP is about getting things done on time, I am really careful about planning to make sure I don't take on more than I can chew. You hear horror stories like people accepting orders from voucher sites to make something like 10,000 cupcakes in a weekend! So provided things are planned, it will be fine. What did you have in mind?"

Aunt Kath and I looked at each other and I gave her a little nod to say she would be best to answer it.

"Well, a prototype to begin with. But beyond that, we are thinking of small batches, so we're not over committed on stock."

"Yes, that's a really good plan. I could definitely help you with the prototype. Then in terms of production, I really like the idea of working in batches. I measure my capacity in terms of hours spent on a job, rather than units produced, because there is so much variability in the work I do. So if I can break your production down into about three stages and do them as batches, it will be much easier for me and cheaper for you. Have you thought about how many you will need each week?"

"Not quite. I guess it could vary, depending on how quickly it takes off."

"The other thing we would need to agree is how much stock you want to hold. Maybe you don't want to hold any and operate on a *just-in-time* basis?"

"Just-in-time?"

"Yes, I think the terminology is from Japan and means that work only gets done when it's needed, so there is never any stock. So, I complete a unit of production only when you receive an order for it. The principle is that holding lots of stock is bad for cash flow. We could still operate that way if we work in batches because I would hold a number of units as work-in-progress and just complete them when you send me orders. That would radically reduce your *lead-time*."

"What do you mean by lead-time?" I asked.

"Well, it's the time it takes me to complete your order. So, say you send me an order for ten duvet covers, and I have to make them all from scratch. That might take me as long as a week depending on what other jobs I have in the queue. But if the material is already cut and all the thread and accessories like buttons or zips have been purchased, then the amount of work needed to complete them is far less, so your lead time would be reduced."

"I still think it would be best for Lucinda to hold some stock," said Aunt Kath, "but only in low volumes."

"Yes, I think that would make sense," said Kate. "That is known as *buffer stock*. The important thing is to ensure you have some economy of scale, as it will really reduce the unit cost and ultimately your profits. What people often don't realise is there are lots of different stages to producing garments. So it starts with the design. Then you have measuring and cutting the cloth. Then I do the stitching, which can vary from job to job. Lastly, the finishing which again can vary. But the time people don't account for within all of that is the set-up. So if I move from making a wedding dress, which requires a much different gauge of fabric and thread to a duvet cover, it takes me a lot of time to adjust the machines. In your case, if I make one king size duvet cover and then a single duvet cover, it will take me time to switch over to a different pattern. But if I make ten king size all together, there is no switching, so I can make more per hour. All of that switching time adds to the cost, since I charge on the basis of hours worked. So, doing jobs in batches really improves efficiency, which then reduces your cost."

"I see. That makes sense. Talking of cost, how much do you charge?"

"My hourly rate is fifteen pounds per hour. But I guess that doesn't help you much in terms of the cost per unit?"

"Not really. That is what I need to think in terms of."

"Well, I can work out some approximate costs if you like, based on different batch sizes. You would only incur some costs once. The initial set-up costs to create the patterns, for example. That's only a few hours work. Then I would work out how many I could produce in an hour and provide you an estimate. Would you want me to source materials as well?"

"Yes, if you can."

"I know all of the main UK based fabric manufacturers, so that should be fine. If I'm holding the fabric stock, I will need them to invoice you directly though, as I don't like to get involved in the purchase of materials. If it helps, I can advise you on what gauge of fabric you need too – are you going for the high-end market or budget?"

"Just standard, really." Then I remembered what Alex had been saying about consumerism and having a USP of 'easy care'. "But, we were hoping for a fabric that doesn't crease too much so it minimises ironing."

"Oh, OK. Yes there is stuff like that on the market. They use it a lot for men's shirts. I can source some for bed linen though. It might cost a little more as they have to treat it, but I do know where we can get hold of some."

"That's great," said Aunt Kath.

"So, I'll do a bit of digging and then email you over an estimated production cost and also some material costs. I presume you want a duvet cover plus two pillows?"

"Yes, exactly," I said. "Shall I write down my email address?"

"Oh yes, that would help! Let me go and get my book."

We exchanged emails, made one final fuss of Jasper and Barry, then made our way home.

What you've covered:

Theme | Amplification
Production | The different methods of production and their appropriateness for different businesses
Productivity | The different ways of measuring productivity and ways in which it can be increased
Purchasing | The importance of controlling stock levels
Purchasing | Different ways of managing stock from traditional to just-in-time
Purchasing | The main components of stock control such as lead-time, buffer stock and re-order level

Memory hook: Stitch-on-time

Kate's 'Stitch on-time' company provides a great memory hook for how a manufacturing business needs to operate. The key to all operations is maximising efficiency and minimising waste. Whilst we mainly think of waste in terms of physical waste, the time it takes workers to be idle or be doing jobs that don't add value, also represents time wasted.

So, key points to remember:

1. *Batch processing* means completing units in batches. Other methods would be *job processing* (completing units one at a time) and *mass production* (or *flow production*) where units get passed along a continuous production line.
2. Production is a key component of efficiency. Since most workers are paid an hourly rate, any time spent idle means they are not adding value to the business.
3. Traditional stock control means the various components to a finished unit are all stored separately. With a just-in-time approach, stock is more limited, so the company only holds enough stock to complete the units in production. As new orders are placed, more stock gets brought in.
4. Lead-time refers to the time it takes to complete an order, whilst buffer stock is an amount of finished items held in reserve.
5. *Work-in-progress* refers to units of production that are part way to completion. So fabric that has been cut, but not yet sewn together, would represent work-in-progress.

Now ask yourself:

1. How do the concepts behind operational management apply to service industries?
2. What are the principal operations in running an airline?
3. Why can holding too much stock and too little stock affect business performance?

Now ask yourself (suggested answers):

1. **How do the concepts behind operational management apply to service industries?**

   Whilst service industries don't make a physical product, they face similar challenges to those organisations that do. Consider a hairdressing salon, as way of example. Their operational objective is to get as many customers through the process as possible. Keeping people waiting too long may result in a loss of business. Having a messy salon may affect customer experience. Running out of products may affect the quality of the service. All of these issues are operational issues.

2. **What are the principal operations in running an airline?**

   An aeroplane needs to take off and land safely and spend as little time as possible on the ground. Therefore, tasks such as re-fuelling, cleaning, moving passengers from and onto the plane, loading and removing baggage and loading food and drink, all need to be done as efficiently as possible. The key measures of success are likely to be: safety, passenger satisfaction, time spent inactive and the seat occupancy rate of the plane.

3. **Why can holding too much stock and too little stock affect business performance?**

   Holding too much stock means that the money spent purchasing it has not been converted into revenue. Therefore, excess stock can damage cash flow – money cannot be available to invest elsewhere in the business if it is tied up in stock. It cannot damage profit, however, since the stock is considered an asset on the balance sheet. Stock also represents a risk in terms of fire or theft.

   Holding too little stock presents a risk in terms of losing customers, if what they want is not available. Also, the opportunity to cross-sell additional products is lost if the additional stock is not available to buy.

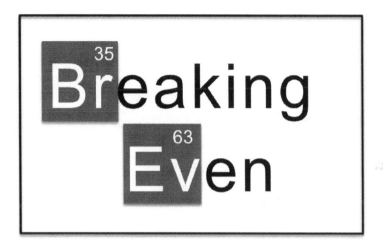

An email from Kate with the production costs arrived in my inbox the next day. I forwarded it on to Uncle Steve and that evening we agreed to get together and discuss them. When I arrived at their house, he was already busy setting up a spreadsheet.

"So, if we accept the estimate from her supplier, the materials are going to cost £10.50 for a single, £14 for a double and £16 for a king. Although who needs a king size bed is beyond me. And then her labour is £8 for a single, £9.50 for a double and £10 for a king."

"They sound reasonable, don't they?" I asked. "I was expecting more than that, to be honest."

"Well, they are about what we were expecting based on your research Lulu, but we should look at other providers before you commit. For now, let's do some maths based on this."

Uncle Steve took me through his spreadsheet, which was already complete for one year of trading. He is a total demon on *Excel*.

"So, I'm taking the start of the year to be four months from now, which gives you time to finish college, and us time to get everything set up. First things first, I've created a sales forecast for the first year. The assumption I've made is that 50% of every item we sell is a double, 25% a single and 25% king. That sound about right to you?"

"I guess so," I said, shrugging my shoulders. My research hadn't extended as far as bed size popularity.

Month	Single	Double	King	Total
1	8	14	8	30
2	8	17	8	33
3	9	18	9	36
4	10	20	10	40
5	11	22	11	44
6	12	24	12	48
7	13	27	13	53
8	15	28	15	58
9	16	32	16	64
10	18	34	18	70
11	19	39	19	77
12	21	43	21	85
Total	**160**	**318**	**160**	**638**

Materials	10.50	14.00	16.00	
Labour	8.00	9.50	10.00	
Delivery	1.00	1.00	1.00	
Cost of goods sold	19.50	24.50	27.00	23.87
Selling price	45.00	55.00	60.00	
Mark-up	131%	124%	122%	
Sales (£)	7,200	17,490	9,600	**34,290**

"In the top table, you see I've forecasted that we sell thirty items in month one. Then in each subsequent month, we grow our sales by 10%, which I've rounded up to whole numbers."

"Which means that in the first year we sell 638 duvet covers?"

"Yes, but we're going to call them items now, since our product is a duvet cover plus two pillows."

"OK. Items. And how much money are we going to make from that?"

"That's the bottom table. I've calculated the *cost of sales*, which covers all *direct costs* - the fabric, plus Kate's labour and a small amount for transportation."

"Transportation? She only lives like two miles away?"

"I know, but once you are running a business, everything needs to be factored in. The materials and labour costs are as given in Kate's email. I've factored in £1 per item for transportation, which is basically the cost of us going two miles each way to collect the stock. So, you'll see that the cost of sales changes by each product variant, which in our case is single/double/king."

"Makes sense. So it costs more to make a king than a double or a single?"

"Exactly. I've then put in some examples of what the selling price might be for each. We can vary these depending on what pricing strategy you choose."

"And what is that '23.87' in the final column, on the cost of sales row?"

"That's the average cost of sales across each of the three variants. So on average, it will cost us £23.87 to make an item, even though in reality it costs more or less depending on which item is made. I've added another line to calculate the *mark-up*, based on each of these selling prices."

"Mark-up?"

"That's the difference between your sales price and the cost of sales, expressed as a percentage. It's calculated as the gross profit margin, divided by the unit cost." Uncle Steve could tell I looked puzzled. "So, for a single, the gross profit margin is £45, minus £19.50, which gives us £25.50. We then divide 25.5 by 19.5, which is the cost of sales, and that works out at 1.31, which is 131%. Do you see?"

"I think so."

"Finally, look here." He pointed to the bottom line of his table. "I've multiplied the number of items we are going to sell in a year by the selling price. So for singles, 160 multiplied by £45 gives us £7,200. We add the three together to give us our all-important annual sales forecast. Or revenue forecast, depending on which term you want to give it."

"£34,290? That doesn't sound much."

"I think it's always best to be prudent in forecasting, Lulu. Too many small businesses radically overestimate their sales. Selling an item per day for the first month or two will be quite an achievement."

"But will I be able to earn a living from that, to help Mum out?"

"Well, let's look at the profit and loss forecast for the first year and see," he said, moving to a new tab in his spreadsheet.

	Year 1
Sales	34,290
Less: Cost of sales	15,231
Gross profit	19,059
Expenditure:	
Salaries	9,750
Rent	840
Utilities	360
Insurance	180
Marketing	5,000
Set-up costs	1,000
Professional fees	400
Total expenditure:	17,530
Operating profit	**1,529**

"So, there's the annual sales forecast we've just calculated. I've then subtracted the cost of sales from that, which gives us our gross profit."

"Hang on, you're confusing me. Didn't Ric, from 'The Horse and Water', call that contribution?"

"Yes, contribution and gross profit are basically the same thing."

"The gross profit looks high. What if we don't make that much?"

"Well, it's based on the figures given to us by Kate, plus the prices we have set based on the what the market is charging, so it should be realistic. Remember that gross profit must always be positive. Otherwise you are not *adding value*."

"Adding value?"

"So the general principle of business is you buy something – raw materials for example; manufacture it into something better, and sell it for more than it cost you to make. That is known as adding value."

"I see. So if our gross profit were negative, we would be selling our items for less than they cost us to make? Which is not good."

"Definitely not. I've then estimated all your fixed costs, which I've called 'Expenditure'. Remember, these were the costs that Ric was going to incur, whether he opened the door of 'The Horse and Water' or not. So when you set your budget, you can change these if you wish."

"Expenditure versus fixed costs. Gross profit versus contribution. All these different terms for the same things? It's getting a bit confusing," I said.

"Well, sorry about that boss. Basically there are two different types of accounting: financial accounting and management accounting. Financial accounting includes creating the Income Statement, also known as the Profit and Loss Account. For that, you talk in terms of gross profit."

"And in management accounting?"

"You talk in terms of contribution. That's the difference."

"OK, I understand. So, let's get back to these figures. You've put marketing as a fixed cost. But I don't have to spend on marketing do I? I mean, if Ric isn't going to open the door of his restaurant, he's certainly not going to spend money on marketing it. So why isn't it a variable cost?"

"Good question. It actually can be both. But in your case, each year you will set aside a pot of money in your budget for marketing. So, I've estimated that at £5,000 for the first year. Every time you make a sale, you don't incur any marketing spend do you?"

"I guess not. But I've spent money on marketing to earn that sale?"

"True, but you do that when you launch your campaigns. Which comes out of your fixed cost pot of £5,000."

"OK, but you said it could be both fixed and variable?"

"Yeah, I did. So, suppose you offer a 5% promotional discount voucher on every item sold in the first 12 months. Then each time you are making a sale, that voucher is being deducted from your revenue. So in that case, it would be a variable cost."

"Oh right, I see. I think. And what about some of these other costs? I'm not going to be paying any rent in the first twelve months, am I?"

"Well, you're going to be running the business from your Mum's house, right? So, technically you can count that as rent. It's better that the business pays your Mum a contribution for rent, rather than you out of your own pocket."

"Why is that, exactly?"

"Well it reduces your operating profit, which means you pay less corporation tax."

"And that operating profit is £1,529. That's final profit, right?"

"Kind of, yes."

"Kind of? You're going to confuse me again, aren't you?"

"Well, it's the final profit from operations. But you will then pay tax on your operating profit if you set up as a limited company. The tax businesses pay is known as corporation tax."

"Which is, how much?"

"Currently it's 20%, but the government can change it at the next budget. So, by paying your Mum rent for the business, the company pays less corporation tax."

"Got it!"

"Anyway, let's not worry about tax just now."

"Suits me! So is a profit of £1,529 any good?"

"I'd say it would be brilliant to achieve that! Most businesses lose money in their first year and some lose money in their second and third years too. Which explains why so many businesses fail. They simply run out of cash."

"Blimey, it's a bit scary when you put it like that."

"Business is a risk, but providing you monitor your finances carefully, you can decide to get out if it looks like the business is not going to work."

"Yeah, but that must be hard once you've committed to it. Must be hard to just quit?"

"Sure. But I guess sometimes you have to be honest and admit something just isn't working. Most of the well-known entrepreneurs you see on TV have failed at some point. But they move on to another venture, until they find one that works."

"So, just to be sure I'm understanding this, with an operating profit of £1,529, we have broken even?"

"Exactly. So at break-even, we would make no profit and no loss. In other words, our total costs exactly equal our revenue. But we have more revenue than costs in this forecast."

"How many items would we need to sell to break even? Just in case we don't do as well as we expect."

"OK, let me write down the formula for that. Can you pass me that pad of paper please, Lulu?" I passed him the pad.

$$\text{Break-even output} = \frac{\text{Fixed costs}}{\text{Contribution per unit}}$$

"So, the total fixed costs are £17,530. But we need to calculate the contribution per unit as currently we only have a total contribution, or gross profit, of £19,059. Dividing that by the number of units sold...which is 638, gives us ... 29.87. So our contribution per unit is £29.87. Which means our break-even output is 17,530/29.87. That is 586.8, which we need to round-up to...587 units."

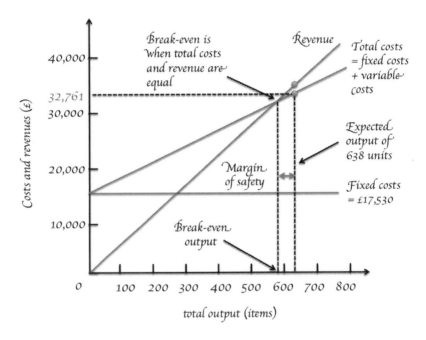

"So, still a lot of units then."

"Let's draw it! Should make it easier to understand." Uncle Steve returned to the pad and started to draw.

"So, here's revenue," said Uncle Steve, pointing at the diagonal line. "You can see it starts at zero, because if we sell nothing, we make no money. And based on our calculations, when we hit our expected output of 638, it should make us £34,290 in revenue."

"OK, that makes sense," I said.

"Fixed costs are easy. That's a straight horizontal line at £17,530. No matter how much we sell, those costs will stay the same. Finally, we have to draw the line for total costs, which equals our fixed costs plus variable costs. Our variable costs are our cost of sales. So, when we make nothing, total costs must equal fixed costs. Mustn't they?"

"Yup, get that. If we make nothing, we have no variable costs. So the total costs line starts at the fixed cost position."

"Exactly. So we need to put a dot at a point we know, which is the 638 units we have forecasted to sell. Let's find 638 on the x-axis. Here. Total costs will be the £17,530 of fixed costs, plus our cost of sales, which at 638 units is £15,231. That sums to £32,761, which is here on the y-axis. So: 32,761 up and 638 along. Drawing a straight line between that point, and the point where total output is zero, creates our line for total costs."

"And the break-even point is where the revenue line hits the total cost line?"

"Spot on. Which is about here on the graph…our 587 units," he said, pointing at the intersection. "And the last thing you need to be aware of is *margin of safety*. That's the difference between our forecasted unit sales and the break-even point, which is 638 less 587… 51 units!"

"Hey, that must be my first maths lesson that's actually made sense!"

"Maybe I missed my vocation?"

"Not in my college you don't. It would be way too embarrassing having my uncle for a teacher."

"Well, it's a bit late for a career change now. So, the last thing we need to think about is cash flow."

"Please let's not do that now, there's only so much my brain can take!"

"Me too. We'll come back to that later."

I thanked Uncle Steve and said my goodbyes to him and Aunt Kath. I left on a high from understanding all those calculations, so decided to pluck up the courage to call Alex on the way home.

What you've covered:

Theme	Amplification
Revenue and costs	Construct and interpret break-even charts and calculate the margin of safety
Revenue and costs	Perform what-if analyses on break-even charts
Income Statement	How to calculate the main components of an Income Statement (Profit and Loss Account)
Income Statement	Calculate gross profit (contribution) and operating profit

---

Memory hook: Breaking Even

In this important chapter, Lucinda learns about break-even and the margin of safety. She also realises that gross profit is equivalent to contribution. The key financial objective of starting a business is to ensure the contribution generated covers all of the fixed costs. Anything above that is operational profit. This involves the delicate balance between setting the right prices and selling in sufficient quantities.

So, key points to remember:

1. Break-even = fixed costs / contribution per unit
2. Margin of safety = forecasted units sold – break-even point
3. Fixed costs are those costs incurred, regardless of how many units are sold. This includes things like rent, rates and insurance premiums.
4. Variable costs can change. Most variable costs are directly related to making the product or delivering the service. However, others such as spend on marketing, are indirect costs.

Now ask yourself:

1. What are some of the approaches Lucinda could take to improve her profit? And what are their associated risks?
2. What are the pros and cons to calculating break-even for a business?
3. Can you think of situations where a business might be willing to sell a product for less than it cost to make (i.e. negative gross profit)?

Now ask yourself (suggested answers):

1. **What are some of the approaches Lucinda could take to improve her profit? And what are their associated risks?**

    - Raising sales prices will generate greater profit – unless it has the negative effect of reducing the volume of sales.
    - Reducing production costs will increase profit – either by negotiating or finding a cheaper supplier. Care must be taken though to ensure this doesn't affect quality.
    - Sourcing cheaper materials will increase profit. Again, quality must be preserved.
    - Operating the business more efficiently could improve profit – such as reducing expenses like utility costs. She could cut back on marketing spend, but this may adversely affect sales volume.

2. **What are the pros and cons to calculating break-even for a business?**

    Pros:
    - The business has a much better knowledge of sales targets.
    - The business can evaluate progress against targets continuously.
    - Bank managers and other potential investors will view this kind of analysis positively.

    Cons:
    - Businesses do not sell all products at a single price. In Lucinda's case, she has three different product types. For a company with 300 products, break-even would be more difficult to estimate.
    - If the business sells its product range at a different ratio than expected, this may affect break-even. For example, suppose Lucinda sells more king-size duvet covers than she predicted, and suppose the gross profit margin in king-size is lower than doubles and singles. This may increase her required break-even level, even though she has sold the same amount of items as she had forecasted.
    - The cost of sales rarely rises in this steady, linear fashion. For example, buying in bulk will often cause unit prices to lower.

- It is only reliable if the data is totally accurate. For example, the company might have a January sale and discount stock. This will affect break-even, since the contribution per unit will be lower.

3. **Can you think of situations where a business might be willing to sell a product for less than it cost to make (i.e. negative gross profit)?**

- **Loss leader** – many businesses sell certain items below cost price to gain customers and/or to entice them to buy other products of higher value in the store – supermarkets frequently do this.
- **Perishable goods** – some products (such as fresh food items) need to be sold before they lose all their value.
- To **generate cash** – if the business needs cash quickly, releasing some stock will help achieve that.
- **Buy-in** – some businesses use a cheap initial price to tie people in to future sales. E.g. mobile phone handsets.
- To eliminate **disposal costs** – for example obsolete machinery or furniture is often sold cheaply if the cost of disposal is high.

CHAPTER 24

Hoverboard Brad

It was a week before I got to see Alex again, although by now we were texting each other through the day. He'd gone to Edinburgh for the weekend to see his best friend from school, so I felt strangely isolated. What if he met some Scottish girl on a boozy night out? Then I got a lovely text, which ended my worries.

I'd told my Mum I was dating him and she asked if I could invite him around for dinner. "Way too soon, Mum!" was my sharp reply.

So it was great to hear he'd returned back safely on the Sunday night and our next chance to be together was the following Tuesday. It was another business trip and again, I had no idea who I was meeting.

The guy was called Brad and he was a hoverboard designer. He looked exactly as I'd imagined a hoverboard designer called Brad looking. He could just as easily have come straight off the beach in Cornwall from a surfing session: a mass of blond hair and a tanned complexion. Handsome, but by now I only had eyes for Alex!

"Brad meet Lucinda – Lucinda, Brad," said Alex, as we walked into Brad's workshop. It was on an industrial estate out of town and had lots of machinery.

"Nice to meet you, Lucinda," was Brad's reply. "I've heard all about your duvet ideas. Nice to know the youth of today are thinking of us oldies who need our beds!"

I laughed, but his stare was just slightly too intimate and I felt strangely uncomfortable. Still, I tried to shrug it off and be cool. "So, what's the story with the hoverboards?"

"Agh, I'm having one of those skanky days when I just want to chuck the whole thing in."

"What's the problem?" asked Alex, looking concerned. Clearly he knew quite a lot about Brad's business.

"It's the age old problem of the tension on the back pad. It keeps flipping over."

I looked confused, so Alex explained. "Brad is trying to create a new hoverboard concept. He's put a motor system under the board that powers a set of air streams. The idea is to create enough upward thrust to lift the board off the ground so it kind of levitates."

"It's more oscillation than levitation," continued Brad. "Upward thrust alone won't be enough on a board this weight. And besides, then it would never move forward. So, I'm trying to create a kind of circular flow of air that creates varying levels of force to counteract each other and push the board forward."

"Wow, it sounds amazing!" I said. It did sound impressive, but it also kind of went over my head.

"Well, there's a major deadline looming and so it's all getting a bit of a stress," said Brad. "Stress and me together doesn't equate to a nice combo."

"Brad wants to exhibit at a major engineering show in Munich next month. He's hoping it will secure the investment he needs to take it into production and get out of R&D mode."

"Research and Development, Lucy," said Brad quickly, before I could acknowledge I knew what it meant from my first meeting with Alex. "A totally overrated way to try and earn a living, if I'm honest." I wasn't sure whether he'd forgotten my name or just decided to shorten it, but I decided not to correct him, even though I hated being called Lucy.

"Ignore him," said Alex. "So basically, R&D is the early stage of a business that's all about trying to prove the product is viable. Like Tesla." He winked at me to show he remembered we'd already discussed it. "Once Brad gets a working prototype, that's been thoroughly tested, he can move onto production."

"Isn't there a danger someone could steal the idea at this Munich show?" I asked.

"Nah, it's cool," replied Brad. "I've got a patent pending, so anyone wants to steal it is welcome. I'll sue their butt off."

He sounded a little arrogant, but I could tell him and Alex were friends, so I smiled politely.

Alex knew I was confused, so he explained it a little more, without making me seem like a complete idiot. "So, when we were talking about your options for intellectual property, Brad has gone down the patent route to protect anyone from stealing his idea. The business of hoverboards is pretty competitive right now, because everyone wants to be the first to create the genuine article."

"Have you seen the Lexus video, Lucy?" asked Brad. I shook my head. "So, basically Lexus spent a fortune creating this video making it look like they'd created a working board. But it was all done through *mag lev* - magnetic levitation, to you and me. So once the board moved away from the magnets they'd laid under the surface, it was game over."

"I thought they made cars?"

"Yeah, it was a stupid publicity stunt. *Guerrilla marketing*, I think you call it, don't you Alex?"

"Absolutely. It's basically creating some crazy stunt to get lots of attention." I could tell Alex was trying hard to make sure I fitted in, whilst explaining everything to me. It was really sweet.

"The coolest part of all this is that Brad has made every single part himself, using a 3d printer," Alex continued.

"I would have to dispute that being the coolest part of it all, young Dr Alex. And as much as I hate to disappoint you, some parts I have had to buy in. Like I know diddly-squat about making motors."

Alex looked slightly embarrassed. "So, you said there was a problem with the back pad?" I asked quickly, trying to diffuse the slight tension in the room.

"That's the problem alright." He held up the board he was working on. "Basically, there are two pads – one at the front, and this bad boy at the back. The rider needs to keep applying pressure to the back and front pads, but not at the same time. Imagine like skiing and moving your weight from the left to the right, but in this case, from the back to the front. That shift of weight causes the two systems of air jets to kick in and then release. This creates the flow of air that's needed to move it off the ground and forward."

"So, have you got it to move yet?"

"Damn right! We've got it to move about five metres. But today, I'm having real issues with the back pad 'cos it's not releasing the flow of air we need. I've created like about 100 different prototypes, each with a slightly different configuration of jets. The best set we had made it move five metres, but then I buggered it all up by adding some extra jets."

"So, once you get it to work, how far can someone go before the power runs out?"

"Well at this rate, five metres!" joked Brad. He was starting to seem a little less cocky. "The other problem I've got is the negative publicity that's come from these segways."

"Segways?"

"Yeah, you must have heard about it? Basically, they released a load of pseudo boards last year. They were just souped up skateboards. And then some kids started to fall off and bam - the press got hold of it. So the risk now is that the media put a major negative spin on the whole hoverboard thing and blows it out of the water."

"Come on Brad, you need to see the ethical side," added Alex.

"Yeah, I get the deal," replied Brad. "Basically Lucy, when you try to invent something, you have to respect the fact people are gonna get concerned the product is dangerous. Particularly when you're trying to get down with the kids."

"Well, I guess I won't have that problem with duvet covers."

Brad laughed. "You never know, Lucy. You just never know. Some old duffer will get their foot stuck in it, fall out of bed and call Injury-Lawyers-R-Us. Bam – he'll sue your pretty butt off. We're all just one shitty day away from a 'no win, no fee' tribunal."

I laughed back awkwardly. "So, who is your target market for this?"

"Oh man, you know I'm just not sure any more, Lucy. Thrill seekers, I guess. People who throw themselves down mountains on bikes, do paintball and drink alcoholic ginger ale. But knowing my luck, it will end up with sides put on it and converted into the next generation mobility scooter."

"Ha, you don't mean that?"

"No Lucy, I don't," he replied sarcastically. "The day it comes to that, they can shoot me. I guess I'm aiming for 0.1% of the population: someone stupid enough to want one and rich enough to part with the 1,500 sov's it'll take to own one. Remember Lucy, 'everyone is not your customer'. That's one of Alex's nuggets of wisdom."

"Seth Godin," added Alex. "A marketing guy called Seth Godin once said that 'everyone is not your customer.' Meaning, don't try to sell to everybody, just the segment you are focused on."

"I think she gets the quote, Alex," cut in Brad. I was beginning to get a little tired of his sarcasm and I could tell Alex was picking up on it.

"Well, I guess we'll leave you in peace Brad, as it's clearly not a good day."

"Yeah, look I'm sorry, Lucy. I'm not normally like this. I've just had a stinker of a day, that's all."

"Don't worry about it. I get them all the time, too," I added with a faint smile.

After shaking hands and a bit of small talk between Alex and Brad, we left and returned to our favourite coffee shop. I was so relieved to get away from Brad. Little did I know what was to follow next!

What you've covered:

Theme	Amplification
Product	A key element of marketing is evaluating who wants your product
Technology	New technology, such as 3d printers, can make business accessible to more people
Research and Development (R&D)	What we mean by R&D and its costs and benefits for stakeholders

Memory hook: Hoverboard Brad

Hoverboard Brad is an example of someone in the innovation stage of business development. He is using new technology to create a prototype that he hopes to showcase at a major European innovation show. All businesses that are trying to make something new will need to go through the R&D phase.

So, key points to remember:

1. 'Everyone is not your customer' means trying not to sell to the whole world, but just your segments of the market. Much like Howard Moskowitz's extra-chunky tomato sauce.
2. Technology such as 3d printers, Computer Aided Design (CAD) and Information Technology (IT), has helped to make business more accessible to more people.
3. Research and Development moves from initial idea generation through to conducting a feasibility study and then on to developing pilots/prototypes and testing.

Now ask yourself:

1. Can you think of any specific industries that depend heavily upon R&D?
2. How might technology developments in robotics affect business and the world in general, in the future?

Now ask yourself (suggested answers):

1. **Can you think of any specific industries that depend heavily upon R&D?**

   Many industries where science and technology provide a competitive advantage rely upon R&D. Two particular industries that do so are Fast Moving Consumer Goods (FMCG) and Pharmaceuticals. The FMCG industry focuses upon household and personal care products; demonstrating that your new innovation brings increased benefits over rivals is of paramount importance in this highly competitive industry.

   In slight contrast, the pharmaceutical industry requires R&D to prove claims on drug efficacy and safety. In order to launch a new drug onto the market, stringent tests must be undertaken to satisfy the regulations that are enforced upon the industry.

2. **How might the technology developments using robotics affect business and the world in general in the future?**

   One of the great future uncertainties is the extent to which robots will replace humans across a variety of work-based functions. In some industries, this has already begun with robots used increasingly in car manufacture, for example. However, Japan recently piloted a hotel that functioned entirely using robots. If this were to become commonplace, then clearly the need for human effort will diminish. This poses a number of questions. In particular, what jobs will humans undertake; how will we acquire goods if few of us are in paid employment and will robots be entitled to the same workplace rights as humans?

   Further questions include: could we ever have a situation where robots manage humans? What will happen if robots develop personalities? Will humans be paid for not working? Would it be legal and ethical to employ robots?

CHAPTER 25

Funky Tease

After we left Brad's workshop, Alex apologised to me for Brad's sarcasm. I said it was fine and that he had nothing to apologise for, but I could tell he felt guilty.

So it came as a bit of a shock, a couple of days later, to receive a text from him inviting me to meet yet another entrepreneur! I was beginning to feel like all of our dates revolved around me meeting his business mates. Still, I knew he was doing it to help me with my own idea. Not wanting to seem ungrateful for his help, I said I'd be delighted to accept.

The following Saturday we boarded a train together and set off to Bristol to meet someone called Sam. Alex never said anything to me about the business on the way down and it felt much more like a date. He was charming and considerate, he'd brought us a packed lunch each and mine was full of all the things I'd told him were my favourite things.

On arriving in Bristol, we soon found our way to Sam's place of work. Alex seemed to know exactly where to go. It was a really fancy building, nothing like Brad's workshop. On the walk, Alex explained that Sam worked in an incubator space set up for new entrepreneurs. They paid low rent in exchange for being in a shared facility with likeminded others and regular access to experts and in-house facilities such as reprographics.

Being on a train together was so nice that I forgot to ask anything about Sam. So, I was a little surprised when Alex introduced me to a woman. I'd somehow expected Sam to be a man. I guessed her to be in her mid-twenties, attractive with long brown hair and bright green eyes. She was easily 5'10 and made me feel like a dwarf. She was almost the same height as Alex.

"Hello Lucinda and welcome to Funky Tease!" she said, whilst offering out the hand on her fully stretched arm. I smiled and shook her hand, remembering someone once telling me that a fully stretched arm indicated a desire to maintain distance, whilst a more bent arm indicated they were more open to you. I decided to pay no notice of that body language claptrap, as she appeared very friendly.

"Funky Tease," I replied tentatively. "Sounds interesting!"

"Alex hasn't explained anything, has he? Typical Alex, bringing you all the way down here, completely blind!" She shot him a mischievous look and he went bright red. It was the first time I'd actually seen him look awkward.

Sam quickly moved on. "So, what he should have told you is that we make limited edition t-shirts and hoodies and stuff like that." She glided her well manicured hands down over her body.

"That's cool!" I said eagerly, realising that her hand gesture meant she was wearing one of her own t-shirts. I looked down at her cropped top, which read: 'I [heart] nerds'. It was tight fitting, showing off her amazing figure.

"Yes, this is one of ours! It's the first one we ever made – for female students, naturally. I purchased the first one off the press and didn't want to wear it for ages, in case it got all tatty. Now I bring it out for special guests!" Again, she seemed to shoot Alex a cursory glance.

She took us into her office space and started to make some drinks from her fancy coffee pod machine. "We've now migrated to one of the biggest spaces here. Soon we'll need to move on, as we've practically outgrown the incubator space; we're always tripping over each other. But for now, I'm happy to stay as the rent is massively subsidised and the people we work around are great."

"How many people do you employ?" I asked.

"There's five of us in total, although I'm the only one that's full-time on the business. I take people from university who are happy to work around their studies. It means I get talented people at low wages, so I'm pretty happy with it. Although it can be a bit of a pain when our deadlines coincide with assignment hand-in dates. Obviously, they have to put their studies first."

The coffee was amazing. I had noticed that Alex had barely said anything since we arrived and that Sam was happy to direct almost everything towards me.

"So, Alex has said that you are looking to start up a similar business. I hope you're not going to steal all my ideas?" She smiled, but I sensed she was only half-joking.

"No, nothing like that!" I replied. "It's not that similar. I plan to make duvet covers."

"Duvet covers? Interesting. What's your USP?"

"It's mainly the design. And the fact they will be easy maintenance through fabric that needs minimum ironing."

"That's a good idea. Ironing a duvet cover can be a right pain because it's so big and bulky. I considered that with our t-shirts, but decided it wasn't so essential. I find the chemical treatment reduces the softness of the fabric, but I guess that's less of an issue with bedding?"

"So, how does your USP work?" I asked, not meaning to ignore her half-question.

"Well, we come up with interesting designs and then limit production to 250. So, anyone who buys a t-shirt can be fairly sure that nobody else where they live will own one too. Unless they buy a job lot, I guess."

"Wow, that's a really good idea!" I exclaimed.

"Thanks Lucinda!" she said, in a voice that sounded ever so slightly fake. "It's working really well, I must admit. The beauty of it is that people pay in advance, but we don't make the batch until all 250 orders have been placed. So it really helps us with cash flow as we're never sitting on any unsold stock."

"What if you don't get to 250?"

"Good question. That was a bit of a problem early on. We had some designs that took weeks to get to 250 and some buyers got a bit irritated. So then we implemented the 'four week rule'. We would produce a batch after four weeks, irrespective of how many orders we had. Due to our success, we haven't needed to evoke that rule for some time."

"That makes sense. So who comes up with the designs?"

"Well I'm a graphic designer, so I put them together. But the team comes up with the ideas. We run a lot of designs seasonally - so we do some Christmassy stuff; we'll have some romantic designs in the run up to Valentine's Day. We recently created a Eurovision t-shirt - totally kitsch and glam-rock! You'd be amazed how quickly that reached 250, mainly because people who were going to Eurovision parties wanted one to wear on the night."

"I bet the limited edition aspect helps?"

"Yes, it really does. We display on the website how many are remaining and once it gets down to about fifty, we see it getting to the magic number within hours. It's quite amazing how much the possibility of missing out on something induces people to act."

"So, where do you promote them?"

"We've managed to build up a large social media following, so that helps a lot. If we do a design for a particular group of people, like the supporters of a football team for example, then we obviously conduct a campaign aimed at them. So we'll allocate an amount of paid social media advertising for each design and then target people through that. The big football teams are quite easy because there are so many potential customers and you obviously make the design appealing to them. We did one recently for triathlons. There's a small band of people around the world who are triathlon mad, and they're all so crazy about it that they just pile in. We hit 250 on that design in under three days, which surprised all of us."

"The concept of appealing to clans of people works really well," said Alex, who had been quiet ever since we arrived. "People are proud of the group they belong to and therefore show it off at any opportunity."

"That's why we started it sweetie, wasn't it?" replied Sam.

We? Sweetie? I felt a surge of awkwardness at the familiarity that existed between them. I had no choice but to ignore it.

"The beauty of it is there's almost an unlimited number of different social groups to appeal to. We'll have about nine or ten designs running at any one time, but we never fail to come up with new ideas. Some of them take a bit of work if they are not very funny or a bit inappropriate. I'll show you our portfolio of designs so far."

She brought over a large album with designs on every page. There were hundreds and they were all awesome. Some were just simple slogans, but others were really detailed designs. Each one looked really unique and impressive, although my head was reeling.

"You are really talented at design, Sam." I said, even though I just wanted to get out of there.

"Aww thanks, that's really nice to hear!"

We hung around for what seemed like an eternity. She showed me around her studio, which was full of lots of different designs that were work in progress. They used an external company to print the garments. Most were screen prints, but some were embroidered. They had a despatch room, but other than that, you would have no idea they retailed t-shirts and hoodies as a business.

We said our goodbyes and headed back to the train station in an awkward silence.

What you've covered:

Theme	Amplification
Business Location	The factors that need to be considered when locating a new business
Technology	The ways in which businesses can exploit social media for promotion
Purchasing	Innovative ways in which businesses can avoid holding any unwanted stock

Memory hook: Funky Tease

Sam at Funky Tease has found a way to totally remove the holding of stock from her t-shirt business. Since a garment is only produced when all its customers have bought one, the business will never hold stock (subject to a decision on returned goods). She was also able to use social media to reach the target audiences for each different design.

So, key points to remember:

1. Locating a business doesn't have to be regionally based. In this case, placing it in an incubator facility meant reduced rent and access to shared facilities.
2. Social media enables businesses to reach out with different messages, to different groups of people. That can be very powerful when selling different product types.
3. Holding stock is bad for cash flow since the materials must be paid for before the finished product is sold. Any way to minimise the amount of stock held is generally a good idea.

Now ask yourself:

1. What are the potential disadvantages to holding no stock?
2. What examples can you think of where organisations have made significant location decisions?

Now ask yourself (suggested answers):

1. **What are the potential disadvantages to holding no stock?**
Some industries deliberately hold little or no stock. Companies who make products to order, for example, will hold no stock. Businesses that hold large volumes of stock are generally those with a quick turnaround of goods. A market trader, for example, would have no business without stock.

Having low stock levels when demand is high can therefore create a significant problem. Companies risk loss of revenue, with customers ultimately going elsewhere. This could impact consumer confidence and loss of goodwill. Equally, if unexpected problems arise in production and there is no stock to fulfil orders, additional pressure is placed on production to rush orders through. This can impact quality control.

2. **What examples can you think of where organisations have made significant location decisions?**
   - Over the last generation, a number of businesses in the western world have decided to re-locate aspects of their business overseas. Customer call centres are a good illustration of this. Many have been moved to places like India where costs such as wages and real estate are very low.
   - With an increasing lack of footfall in town centres, a number of businesses have either relocated their shops to retail parks or replaced their physical premises with an online store.
   - A number of large American corporations, such as Amazon and Starbucks, have re-located their European headquarters to territories that are financially advantageous. Specifically, this has helped them to pay lower rates of tax. Historically, the Isle of Man and the Channel Islands have been seen as tax havens for businesses.
   - Some businesses expand into countries with strongly anticipated future growth. Examples include areas of the Middle East such as Dubai, Qatar and the UAE. Emerging territories like South Africa and South East Asia are other examples.

CHAPTER 26

A need for privacy

As the train left the station, I turned to Alex. "Why didn't you warn me that you and Sam used to see each other? Sweetie!"

Alex was flushed red. "I'm so sorry. I didn't think it was relevant and I didn't think it would matter. It was ages ago and pretty brief. One summer, in fact."

"It doesn't matter, Alex? The fact is she made it quite clear that you two had history and I had no idea about it. It's like you deceived me."

"I know, I'm really sorry. I should have said something."

"Or not taken me to meet her at all?" I was getting more angry and jealous. "It's like you need to show off all your business mates to me and if that includes your pretty ex-girlfriends all the better, because it shows me what a stud you are."

"Hey, that's not fair. I'm introducing you to these people to help you with your own business."

"Yeah, I get that. But do you not think that maybe, just once, I want to be with you and not your line of work?"

"Fine, I won't introduce you to any more of my network."

"Agh! I'm not saying that. Why don't you get it? I'm just saying, your gorgeous ex-girlfriend who clearly still has feelings for you, isn't a good choice when we're just getting to know each other."

"She doesn't have feelings for me and I don't have feelings for her. We're just friends. It sounds to me like you're jealous."

"Maybe I am, but you shouldn't be putting me in a situation where I'm going to feel like that. It's normal as a woman, Alex, to feel insecure around someone who is all legs and boobs and used to sleep with your boyfriend."

"Is that what I am? Your boyfriend?"

"Oh great, thanks a lot! So now you're saying that what I thought we had, is all in my mind? Am I just another one of your network, Alex?"

"No, it's just we haven't really talked about commitment yet."

"Commitment? I'm not asking you to marry me! You really need to figure out how to make a girl feel special. Your arrogant friend Ash is right about you. Why don't you get off at the next stop and go back to your ex. I'm sure she won't want any sort of commitment."

"But…"

"But nothing. Just stop talking, will you. I've just realised you're an idiot that I'm stuck on this stupid train for another hour with. So, unless you want me to go to another carriage, just stop talking."

He did as I asked and we both realised by the sniggers and the darting looks that the ten or so people in the carriage had been listening intently to our argument.

Getting home felt like an eternity. Eventually, the train pulled up at the station and I couldn't get off quickly enough. Alex apologised again and asked if we could meet in the week with no ex-girlfriends. I told him he could add me to that list.

What remained of the weekend involved me skulking around the house. I told my Mum what had happened and she agreed he was a total idiot. Bizarrely, the more she tore a strip off him, the more I felt like defending him. As I reflected on the meeting, Sam clearly knew there was something between us, which meant that Alex must have told her about us. So looking back, it was her who stirred things up by making it clear they had a past. She wanted me to know about them, so maybe she was jealous of me? Or just a cow? I decided she was both.

The hours passed and I couldn't face anything. I mainly watched repeats on TV. I had a long chat with Lucy on the phone. For once, she had no dramas of her own with Bruce, so we talked mostly about Alex, who she asserted was a total sleazebag that should go and crawl back into the hole from which he came.

On Sunday morning, I received a phone call from Brita. She'd been looking through the files on her PC and had found an old spreadsheet with customer details from her days of running Duvet Days. She said they were a few years out of date, so some people may have moved on, but many did have email addresses. She told me I was welcome to contact them and introduce my business if I wanted. She had worried about data privacy, but thought it would be OK if I specifically mentioned her. And then she said I was welcome to name my business Duvet Days too. That didn't sound so bad?!

And in that time, I heard nothing from Alex. Not a text, or a phone call. Nothing. So clearly I meant precious little to him after all. Maybe he'd gone back to see Sam and get things back on track. They deserved each other.

Then on Sunday evening, I received a text, inviting me out for a drink. It was from Comedy Will.

What you've covered:

Theme   Amplification
Data Privacy   The ethics of sharing personal data with other
                         organisations

Memory hook: A need for privacy

This short chapter is mainly focused on Lucinda's personal life. However, the issue of privacy on the train is a prelude to the important theme of data privacy in business. The phone call with Brita raises an important obligation businesses have. Was it correct for Brita to allow Lucinda to contact her old customers, when they hadn't 'opted-in' to receiving third party communication?

So, key points to remember:

1. *Data protection* is a legal requirement of businesses not to share customer data with third parties, unless they have explicitly agreed to it.
2. Many people believe that businesses could be more ethical in how they manage customer data. For example, the receipt of 'nuisance phone calls' is an example of businesses taking advantage of people inadvertently allowing their personal data to be made available.
3. In addition to *data protection*, the law on managing data also includes *data preservation* – ensuring data is up to date and *data disposal* – removing data from servers when required.
4. New EU legislation is due to be imposed from 2018 (The General Data Protection Regulation). The UK's future exit from the EU may necessitate this, and other laws, being addressed by UK government.

I accepted the invitation and met Will in a pub the following night. Alex had told him what had happened with Sam. He said he'd reprimanded Alex, telling him he was a total idiot. He actually used much stronger words than that. And then he said something completely beautiful.

"Look Lu, I personally think you and Alex could be great for each other. I am certain that he has no feelings for Sam and that he took you to meet her purely to help you. I hope you get over this and have a great time learning about each other. But if you don't manage to do that, I have to tell you now that I think you are amazing and I would risk my friendship with Alex to have a chance with you myself."

I was shocked by what he said, but could tell he was being sincere. "Will, that's so lovely of you to say." I paused, trying to find the right words to communicate how I felt. "I think we'll have to see what the future holds. I mean, it's all been a bit of a whirlwind, to say the least. I hardly know Alex if I'm honest, so I don't know what to do. And you...you seem lovely too…"

"It's alright Lu, I understand how freaky it must be for you. Alex doesn't know I've asked to meet you tonight. I'm not trying to steal you from him, honest. Guess I just want you to know that you've made a big impression on both of us."

"Thanks, Will."

There was an awkward silence, as neither of us quite knew what to say next. We both picked up our drinks at the same time and then laughed as each of us realised what we were doing.

"So, how's the comedy website coming on?" I asked.

"Oh, it's good. I've designed most of the pages now. I'm just struggling a little to figure out how to monetize it."

"Monetize it?"

"Yeah, like how to make money from it."

"Oh, I see. Well, weren't you going to pay people to advertise their comedy nights with you?"

"Yes, that's one way of doing it. Another would be to make it a proper booking website and take a proportion of the entrance fee." I could tell he looked less enthusiastic about this idea.

"That sounds good! Why not do it that way?"

"Well firstly, the website becomes more complicated to build. But the bigger problem is it doesn't fit all venues. Some venues offer free entrance and the comedy is just a way to get people through the door. Others have their own booking site and mine would need to sync to that. It might put quite a few off joining us."

"Oh I see." I tried to be critical of the other approach to show I was thinking in the right way. "I guess the problem with the other way is you don't want it becoming too much of an advertising site?"

"Exactly. I don't want endless pop-ups. I'm happy to build it as a directory site with a search facility. The venues I've spoken to so far have all said they will go with that. And then of course, there's always the revenue from promoting new acts."

"Oh yeah, the video uploads! I love that. So have you done any forecasting yet?"

"Yeah, I've had to do that to justify it to myself as much as anything. Alex...sorry, I know I shouldn't mention that...anyway, him, has always said not to build forecasts to fit what you want to happen. That way, you will be fixing the numbers to what you want, rather than what you will get. But anyway, he's a douche, so I've done it anyway. What does he know? Ha!"

"Totally agree with you. On all counts! So, what have you come up with?"

Will brought out his notebook and showed me his forecasts. He'd estimated one hundred venues in six months, each paying a £25 annual promotion fee.

"So, how will you get each venue to pay £25?"

"OK, my plan is this. I'll give them six months to promote their comedy nights as a free trial. After six months, they will pay the £25 annual fee. This covers them for the next six months. Plus this rate will be a 75% discount. So in the following year, I should be able to charge £100 per venue. At that price, it will become a proper money making enterprise."

I paused and screwed my face up a little. He could tell I didn't like it.

"I'm not sure that's the right approach, Will. I think you're in danger of underselling your site. Once someone starts paying £25, their expectation will be that's what it's worth. Suddenly, £100 will seem overpriced."

"I get that, but I've got to be realistic. In the first six months, I'm not going to generate the web traffic to make £100 value for money. It will take a full year to build up the traffic to justify a website at that price-point."

"I'm still not convinced. I think the difference between £25 and £100 is too great. Why don't you go with £50 and say the first six months was free? That means they are paying £50 for six months, so when they pay £100 for twelve months, it will not be a shock."

"Hey, that works Lu! I get that. Yeah, that's probably the best way forward. Nice one!"

"No worries. I'll take my fee as another half of cider!"

"Want some crisps thrown in too? A half of cider is underselling yourself!"

"Yeah, make it a half of cider for what I've helped with in the last ten minutes, and the crisps for what I'm going to help with in the next ten minutes!"

As Will got the drinks, I reflected on the increasing self-confidence I was feeling in my business thinking abilities. When he returned, we moved on to considering his revenue from the video uploads. He was charging £25 per introduction.

"Again, I think that's too cheap Will."

"But many of these venues won't be able to pay much more than that. I don't want to price myself out of the market."

"OK, but how much would they normally pay to book someone? I bet £50 minimum. And are you giving a cut to the performer?"

"No way. They are getting the breakthrough gig they need. They'll happily do it for free."

"Will, you said it yourself: there are open mic sessions up and down the country. If they're good enough, they will eventually get spotted. Far better to let them at least take some money and then they will stay on your site for longer."

"Urm, I'm not sure. I'll give that one some more thought."

"Why don't you ask some of the venues you have a relationship with, how much they would be prepared to pay for an act they saw on your site? That's like the focus group I did with my Aunt's book club people. I learnt lots from their feedback."

"Yeah, that sounds like a plan. Market research, right."

Will and I talked some more and then he walked me home. He gave me a big hug outside and a gentle kiss on the cheek. I felt my trust in men had been partially restored.

What you've covered:

Theme	Amplification
Pricing strategies	The impact of pricing decisions on a business and its stakeholders
Pricing strategies	Different pricing strategies to justify an appropriate price, e.g. psychological pricing
Promotion strategies	The promotional strategies businesses can use

---

Memory hook: The Price is Right

Will has the task of deciding how to price and promote his service. His problem is similar to many other start-ups: convincing customers of the value of their product/service before they have experienced it. Incentives are a common way businesses overcome this. However, the business must be careful not to anchor customers' expectations to that price forever.

So, key points to remember:

1. Setting a certain price for a product provides customers with an expectation of what that product is worth. It then becomes difficult to substantially raise the price in the future. One way businesses overcome this is set a low promotional price and then 'lock' subscribers into a contract that includes a price hike in the future.
2. *Psychological pricing* means making a product appear to be cheaper through various means. For example: £9.99 appears cheaper than £10. 'Buy one, get one free' is another type of psychological incentive. Promoting a deal for 'print magazine only subscription' at £55 and 'print magazine with internet subscription' at £60, makes the second deal sound like a better offer than it perhaps really is?
3. Businesses often discount their product or service during the growth stage of the product life cycle to incentivise people to get on board.

Now ask yourself:

1. Can you think of any industries where setting a low price is not a good idea?
2. What other reasons exist for people to support a business idea before it becomes 'fashionable'?

Now ask yourself (suggested answers):

1. **Can you think of any industries where setting a low price is not a good idea?**

    - **Luxury goods** are expected to be expensive since they are exclusive. The type of people who can afford to purchase them may be less likely to do so were the price heavily reduced.
    - If a business expects **small orders** then a low price is not going to help since the business is unlikely to generate economies of scale.
    - Environments where there is **low competition** or a strong need to purchase, typically inflate prices. For example: catering at theme parks and concerts with no other choices available; or motorway service stations where the next stop could be many miles away. Customers at these locations expect to pay higher prices.
    - In **technology sectors**, prices come down over time. Therefore prices start off high during the growth phase. For example, computer game consoles reduce gradually in price.

2. **What other reasons exist for people to support a business idea before it becomes 'fashionable'?**

    - People may have a significant **personal attachment** to the product – for example, environmentalists purchase things according to their beliefs and values and not what is fashionable.
    - **Early adopters** like to have something before other people do.
    - Some people enjoy **testing new innovations** or being seen to be different.
    - **High risk-takers** will buy something new because it excites them.

CHAPTER 28

Return on investment

It felt like ages since I'd seen Uncle Steve, so I went around for coffee the next night. Mum said he'd had a few work issues of his own to deal with.

"So what's going down with you?" I asked over coffee and Aunt Kath's homemade biscuits. "Mum says you have something big going on at work?"

"Oh that," he replied. "Not big exactly. I've been presented with an opportunity to buy-out one of my competitors, that's all."

"Uncle Steve, you always play everything down! That's huge. What are you going to do?"

"I've no idea. At first, it was a straight no. But then we've looked the figures over and it's actually a pretty good offer."

"We?"

"I've had my accountant check it out."

"So, how much will it cost to buy them out?"

"Well that's a fairly direct question, Lulu! But as it's you, I'll tell you. He took a sip of coffee and paused for dramatic effect.

"Go on then, spill!"

"£1.75m."

"Are you serious? Wow, Uncle Steve! If I'd known you were worth that much, I'd have been a lot nicer to you all these years!"

"Too late now, we've written the will. It's being split equally between your brother, cousin and an orphanage in Romania."

I poked him in the arm. "How do you know that's a good deal though? Maybe you could negotiate lower?"

"Well, we've calculated the return on investment over a five year period. It shows the price is quite attractive already."

"How do you calculate that?" I asked reluctantly. I had always been nervous around figures.

"Easy. You divide operating profit by the amount of capital invested and multiply it by 100 to express as a percentage."

"Whoa, hold on! That might be easy to you, but my brain is wired differently. What's the purpose of doing that?"

"Well, I need to know how much of the money we're putting in is going to come back to us. So I'm calculating profit as a percentage of our investment."

"Oh right, makes sense now."

"Good. So we've estimated their total operating profit over the next five years to be £550,000. Divide that by £1.75m and what do you get?"

I shrugged. "What am I, the human calculator?"

"It comes to around 31%. Over five years."

"That doesn't sound good? Surely you want it all back?"

"Well, we'd still own the company remember. So that 31% is effectively interest."

"So it's good, then?"

"To decide whether it's good, you have to consider how else I could invest it. So, say I have £10,000 sitting in a savings account at my bank and it earns me a measly 2% interest a year. Suppose instead, I decide to invest that £10,000 in your duvet cover business. What did we calculate your potential operating profit to be last week?"

"I don't know, it seems like there are about ten different definitions of profit going on! What is operating profit, again?"

"OK, so gross profit is revenue, less the cost of sales. Operating profit is revenue less all costs of running the business. Then, net profit is operating profit less any tax and interest paid. Let's draw it."

```
R        Revenue
↓        - Cost of sales
G        Gross profit
↓        - All other costs
O        Operating profit
↓        - Tax & interest
N        Net profit
```

"R-G-O-N. Remember that and you won't go far wrong. So, let's say your operating profit came out at £1,500. At that level, my annual return on investment would be 15%, because £1,500 divided by £10,000 is 15%. So compared to earning 2% in the savings account, your business would be a much more attractive investment."

"So, why does anyone put their money in savings accounts?"

"Think about. What's the danger of investing in your business?"

"That you have to work with me every day?!"

"There is that. But also…it might go bust. At least in the bank, I have a guaranteed rate of return and I can be pretty much certain I won't lose my money."

"So that offer to buy the other company is good because 31% is more than you would get from a savings account?"

"Kind of yes. Although I'd have to borrow money to raise that amount of cash, so the cost of raising the capital needs to be accounted for."

"Are you going to do it then?"

"My accountant values their business a bit higher than that, but if we do it, we're still going to come in with a lower offer."

"Hang on, if they're prepared to sell the company for less than it's worth, it sounds a bit dodgy. How do you know there isn't some problem they're hiding?"

"Good point, but I know the owner and it's all above board. They have genuine family reasons for selling up."

"So, it's a bargain then? Great! Maybe you should agree or they might go elsewhere?"

"Yes, but it's not that straightforward. We have something they don't – two big clients. Both of which keep growing exponentially. But they have a lot of smaller clients. So, going from managing two clients to many, will cause us lots of problems. I don't fancy paying a premium for the privilege. And we don't want to risk losing our two big fish through shoddy service from chasing around after their small fish."

"And you could make more profit in the future when those two clients get even bigger?"

"Exactly. Those two clients account for over 70% of our annual turnover. Turnover is another word for revenue," he said, noticing my puzzled expression at yet another new keyword. "I managed to secure those contracts years ago and they've stayed with us ever since. But they've grown into much bigger firms now, so they are very valuable."

"Why do they stay with you? Surely this other company with lots of clients has tried to steal them?"

"They have, many times! But both companies have remained loyal to us because they attribute a lot of their success to the work we did for them at the start. Thankfully, there is still some honour in the business world."

"I get it. So if you went out and bought this other company, you would have the headache of lots more clients?"

"Precisely. Having lots of customers in business isn't always a good thing. Currently, our operating profit margin is around 10%, but it has the potential to grow higher than that in the future. Their operating profit margin is around 8%, even though they have more clients and are technically a bigger company."

"What is profit margin?"

"Profit margin is the ratio of profit to revenue. So, our revenue last year was just under £1.4m. Divide our operating profit of £135,000 by that and you get something close to 10%."

"But why do they earn less profit than you if theirs is a bigger company than yours?"

"No, they earn more profit than we do. But their ratio of profit to revenue is lower than ours. So because we are smaller, we are a lot more efficient than them. For example, we don't need to invest much in marketing and we don't have the service departments they will have such as Human Resources. I don't have a Finance department like they do, I just pay my accountant."

"OK. I understand. Why don't you decline this opportunity to take over them and steal some of their best clients? It sounds like you are better than them anyway?"

"I suppose I'm not that cut throat. Besides, our quality of life is pretty good now. It took years of sweat and tears to build up the company.

Now, I'm just happy to take it easy. Buying this company would tie us into more years of hard work, just as cherry picking their best clients would. Whereas, in a few years we could sell our business, pay off the mortgage, buy the villa in Portugal your Aunt Kath has been dreaming about for years and still have enough to take you, your Mum and crazy brother out for a celebratory pizza."

Uncle Steve knew I loved pizza. "Pizza. Any size we want?"

"Any size."

"Then don't accept!"

We laughed. Then he asked me how things had been going with me. I told him all about the stuff with Alex and Sam, which felt weird because Uncle Steve and me didn't usually talk girl-boy stuff.

"Anyway, you'd better speak to your Agony Aunt for advice on what to do with him. She'll be back soon. But for what it's worth, I say go and speak to him and go with your gut instinct. You have to make a few mistakes at your age; it's part of the deal. I'm still paying for mine now."

"Uncle Steve! You are so lucky to have Aunt Kath. Nobody else would put up with you."

"Nobody else got a chance. She elbowed her way in and slammed the door on the competition. Knew a good thing when she saw one."

"Uncle Steve, your wedding photo up there says it all. You've got a mullet and Aunt Kath looks beautiful. I say you got the deal of the century there and then, never mind this company buy-out."

"Mmm, maybe. Anyway, there's someone I want you to meet. He's a pal of mine, a marketing guru. Can I take you around later this week?"

I heaved a sigh. "Another one. I feel like my life is one meeting with a business acquaintance after another. I haven't even got a business plan yet. And everyone I meet is way more talented or further on with their business than I am."

"It's good to get all this experience. And he's a really interesting guy, you'll like him."

"But Uncle Steve, I've done interesting to death. Aside from crazy t-shirt lady, I've met a guy designing hoverboards and a man who's intent on taking over the world of comedy websites. Who fancies me, as it turns out, but that's another story. Does nobody just start a plumbing business any more?"

"Ha! Well, go to one more for me. We need to see him because you need to think about your marketing strategy before writing the business plan."

"Agh! If I knew starting a business was so much hard work, I'd have just stuck to more college."

"Nothing worth having comes easy, Lulu."

"But that's it. I'm now seriously questioning whether I've got anything good anyway. I mean, compared to hoverboards and comedy websites, duvet covers are a bit…well, boring aren't they?"

"Everyone likes going to bed Lulu, even me. We spend about a third of our lives up there. So people are always going to want duvet covers. Hoverboards will be in the cupboard under the stairs after a month."

Aunt Kath came in to break up the discussion and I agreed to go and meet this marketing guru. On my way home, a text from Alex arrived.

Hi Lu, I'm so sorry about last week. I was a complete idiot. Will you please meet me for a drink so we can talk about it? Alex x

I wanted to answer straight away but decided to keep him stewing. It felt so good to hear from him though!

What you've covered:

Theme	Amplification
Ratio analysis	Calculate and interpret profit margins
Ratio analysis	Understand reasons why one business can have lower profit margin than another, yet make more profit
Ratio analysis	Calculate 'Return On Investment' (ROI) and understand how it is used to value a business decision

---

Memory hook: Return on investment

Uncle Steve's decision on whether to pursue this opportunity to buy a competitor is a good hook for recalling the importance of ratio analysis. The opportunity to acquire another business is an example of an investment in a non-current asset (one that will remain in the business for more than a year). Other non-current assets include items such as machinery, property and vehicles. *Return On Investment (ROI)* calculates how much additional income Steve's company should receive annually from purchasing the competitor.

So, key points to remember:

1.   Recall R-G-O-N for the three different types of profit.
2.   Return on investment = (Operating profit x 100) / Capital invested
3.   Profit margins are equal to (Profit / Revenue) x 100. So:
     - Gross profit margin = (Gross profit / Revenue) x 100
     - Operating profit margin = (Operating profit / Revenue) x 100
4.   Assets can be current, such as stock or cash in the bank, or non-current, such as property, vehicles or other businesses, like in this example.
5.   Capital expenditure refers to the amount of money required to invest in a non-current asset.

Now ask yourself:

1.   What adverse factors could arise in the future that a current ROI calculation might not have accounted for?
2.   Why might a company decide to save money rather than invest?
3.   What is meant by 'opportunity cost' and why is it relevant to this chapter?

Now ask yourself (suggested answers):

1. What adverse factors could arise in the future that a current ROI calculation might not have accounted for?

Return on investment (ROI) comprises just two variables – operating profit and capital invested. So the only two things that can affect ROI are those two variables. Operating profit can be impacted on by either lower than expected revenue, or higher than expected costs. A number of factors could cause both of these outcomes. Capital invested - well this takes place at the outset, so cannot be impacted in the future unless additional investment is required down the line.

2. Why might a company decide to save money rather than invest?

- They may feel that the economy is about to nosedive and therefore investment opportunities should be deferred.
- They may anticipate some internal problems ahead that may benefit from having cash in the bank.
- If interest rates are high, then the return from savings could exceed the return from investment.
- They may feel uncertain about what needs investment and prefer to wait until the situation becomes clearer.

3. What is meant by 'opportunity cost' and why is it relevant to this chapter?

When people or businesses have options on which direction to take, opportunity cost refers to the cost of declining the alternatives. For example, a business owner may have two options: A and B. A is worth £2,000 and B is worth £1,500. Suppose B is guaranteed, but A contains risk. If they decide on A and it comes off, the actual gain is £2,000, but the real gain is only £500, since they would have received a guaranteed £1,500 with option B.

CHAPTER 29

Orchid Marketing

I managed to hold back on replying for a full two hours! That felt long enough for him to know I wasn't a walkover, but sufficiently short to satisfy my own desire to maintain contact. I told him I was still really upset about what had happened, but I might be prepared to meet for a drink, once I'd calmed down. I said I didn't know when that would be.

In the meantime, the meeting with Uncle Steve's marketing guru came around faster than I expected. He was going away on a business trip from Friday, but could see us for an hour on the Wednesday.

So later that day, we arrived at his office. It was a large glass fronted building that I immediately noticed was called the 'Orchid Studios'. I had bought Mum one for Christmas and she had been desperately trying to keep it alive ever since.

"Lucinda, this is Elliott," said Uncle Steve, as he approached us in his foyer. He was a smartly dressed man in his thirties, exuding confidence and warmth.

"Lovely to meet you," he said as we shook hands. "Come on through."

As we navigated our way through his wide open-plan office, into a glass-fronted room at the back, I was struck by the continuing array of orchids everywhere. Various different species were displayed on virtually every desk.

"I see you like orchids," I asked nervously.

"Yes, we adore them here. Our company name is Orchid Marketing. Do you know much about them?"

"I got one for my Mum for Christmas. She's hopeless with plants and I was told they are quite easy to maintain."

"Indeed they are! They are very resilient plants. But they have other fantastic qualities too. If you look up there, you can see the four key aspects we particularly love about orchids." He pointed to a fantastic looking set of giant posters on the wall.

"They grow from extremely small seeds you see. That fits well with us because assisting new start-ups to grow from nothing is what we are all about. Then the orchid flower tends to resupinate, meaning that it points upwards. We look for all our businesses to think ambitiously," he said, whilst pointing up to the ceiling. "The orchid flower has bilateral symmetry. We use that to denote the symmetry of our relationship with our clients. They must take on board what we advise them, otherwise we are wasting their money."

We arrived in his office. "And the fourth?" I asked, noting that he had only described three of the four features, each with slightly corny metaphors.

"Oh yes. Well look around you: the fantastic array of bright colours and unusual shapes. Even though we ask our clients to listen to our expertise in marketing, every business must have its own personality and be unique from the rest. You will never see two orchids the same and that is what makes us all want to get up in the morning. The diversity of ideas we come across every day."

Trying to conceal a faint snigger, I turned away by accepting his invitation to sit in a really comfortable armchair. It felt nothing like a business meeting, more like an interview for some kind of bizarre reality TV show.

"Anyway, I've known your uncle for years now and he tells me you are a chip off the old block?!"

"Oh, please don't say that!" I replied jokingly, looking at Uncle Steve.

"She has her Mum's looks and my brains," cut in Uncle Steve.

"What a relief to have your Mum's looks," he laughed. "But seriously, he's told me about your business idea and I have to say I'm intrigued. Your uncle has done lots for me in the past, so I'm happy to meet up with you a few times and talk through the marketing side of things. If you want to, of course?"

"Yes, that would be really great," I said nodding my head, probably too vigorously. I have a habit of making exaggerated movements when nervous.

"OK, here's what I know. You have an idea for a duvet cover that is original in design and easy to care for. You are looking to build it up by making small batches to reduce your stock burden."

"That's pretty much it, yes."

"Right. Well it sounds like a good initiative. But I'm going to ask you the same question I ask everyone in your position. The world is full of bright ideas sitting on shelves in garden sheds and workshops. Yet most of them, we never find out about. How is Mrs Smith, a hundred miles down the road, going to find out about yours?"

I paused. "Well I plan to use social media mainly and possibly create a selling page on Amazon."

"OK. That's a start, but it needs more behind it than that. Let me go back a step. What would you say the role of 'marketing' is?"

I thought back to all my conversations with Uncle Steve and Alex. The two things that came to mind were 'promoting things' and 'enabling sales to take place'. I put on a confident face and outlined those thoughts within a slightly more longwinded answer.

"Not bad. You are kind of right. Marketing is the link between the business and the customer." He got up and drew two boxes on a whiteboard. He inserted the words 'business' and 'customer' in each box and connected them with a line, above which he wrote 'marketing'. "But that's not enough, is it? That's like saying the purpose of a car is to get you from A to B."

"But isn't it?"

"Well yes, but not when we go to buy one. For that, we need answers to questions like how often we go from A to B? How quickly do we need to get there? How much damage to the ozone layer are we willing to incur doing it? And how comfortable do we want to feel on the ride? It's those questions that decide which car we want to buy. Which all brings us back to one thing…" He pointed his pen at the 'customer' box.

"So marketing is about understanding the customer?"

"Exactly! And not just understanding her. Or him. But building up a relationship with her. Or him. You see, when I buy a duvet cover from you, we have engaged in an exchange. You have received my hard-earned money and in exchange I have received my purchase. Now, we assume I wanted a duvet cover, which I probably did. But if I just wanted a duvet cover, why did I choose yours? Why not just buy the first one I could find in Tesco or the first one that came up in a Google shopping search?"

"Because you liked the look of mine?"

"Urm, yes and no." He paused. "Let me explain something. Products and services basically fall into one of two categories – 'mass market' or 'niche'. If you put your duvet cover in the mass market, then you need to differentiate either on the strength of your brand, the price you charge or the quality of the product. It is usually assumed that price and quality are on two axes. If you are high on price, you are high on quality; low on price, low quality. Brands build up over time and can fall into either category. The point is, if you are in the mass market, you need to fall somewhere into these categories. Sitting in the middle doesn't help you one iota, because you offer no discernible advantage."

"But I don't want to sit in the middle. And I don't have a well-known brand. My USP is the unique design of the duvet cover."

"But does the customer want that?"

"Yes. If they hate changing duvet covers in the usual way."

Another pause. "How often do you change a bed? Once a week? Twice a week?"

I didn't want to admit to once a week, so I said twice a week.

"Right, and how long does it take you to make a bed?"

"About ten minutes."

"So that's twenty minutes a week, if you are being diligent. And honest," he said, smiling ruefully. "Do you know how many minutes there are in a week?"

"No."

"10,080. Now, I'm not sure what percentage 20 minutes is of that, but it's quite small. So is the extra investment in your duvet cover going to be worth my while? I'm assuming you will charge more for this new design, right?"

I felt a bit stung by this attack on my idea, so I retaliated. "Well not really. And anyway, twenty minutes might not seem like a long time over a full week, but it seems like an eternity when you are there fighting it. We probably don't spend that much time washing dishes in the sink, but we'd all rather put them in a dishwasher."

"That's a really good point, Lucinda! And by challenging my comment, you have just asserted the emotions some people have when they are putting a duvet cover on. But if your vacuum cleaner breaks down beyond repair, you probably go online and look for a replacement. Not many people, after making a bed are going to go downstairs and buy a replacement duvet cover, are they? If you are being honest. Therefore when people see your product, you need them to immediately recall how they felt the last time they made the bed, which might be days ago. You need that anger to come flooding back. That's the marketing bit. It's what we call market orientation, as opposed to product orientation." He got up and pointed at the line between the business and the customer on his whiteboard.

"But I don't want to be in the mass-market," I said, ignoring his latest piece of advice. "I am quite happy to start small and grow."

"Yes I get that. So you are in the 'niche' area. Fine. But what I'm asking, is whether your innovative design is sufficiently niche?"

"Well, I think it is. Not many people are making them. And anyway, it's not just the design. I also want them made using easy to iron fabric."

"OK, so you are going for the 'people in a hurry' segment?"

"Yes, I suppose so."

"You see, it comes back to the relationship thing. If I've just bought one of your duvet covers, you want to maintain that relationship with me so I buy more in the future, or recommend you to a friend. But am I going to be quite so keen to have a relationship with your business? I mean, I don't know who made the duvet cover on my bed at the moment, but I'm certainly not connected on Facebook to them."

"But that's because the duvet cover on your bed hasn't just made your life easier!"

"No, that's a fair point. Just humour me for a moment. I have a client. A husband and wife couple to be precise. They run a modest little hotel with about five bedrooms. Now, you and everyone else would say they belong in the hospitality industry, right? Except, we never consider any aspect of their service to be remotely connected with 'hospitality'. Why do you think that might be?"

"They run a really rubbish hotel?"

"Ha! That's a good answer. Fortunately for them, it's a nice hotel with lots of contented guests who return regularly. But each and every one that does, all has something in common with the others: they are passionate about the environment. You see, the building is totally carbon neutral and pretty much everything is recycled. And therefore, the people that go there, really don't care too much about being waited on, so your basic hospitality principles don't really apply."

"OK. So are you saying I should not be in the bedding industry?"

"No, you are in the 'people in a hurry' industry. You see, the world is changing a lot Lucinda. Back in the good old days when your Uncle was your age, we pretty much only bought things when we needed them. Therefore, everything was categorised into industries – food and drink, automotive, leisure, clothing; you name it. Nowadays, industries exist based upon the values we hold and the lifestyles we have. So the people who buy your duvet cover are just as likely to spend their money on say, a dishwasher. This means you might not actually be competing with bedding manufacturers at all."

I thought about it. "That's really weird. But kind of makes sense."

"Good! It should do. Let me ask you another question. Is the bedding industry growing?"

"Urm…maybe. If we're living longer."

"OK, but it's probably not growing rapidly is it?"

"No, I guess not."

"Right. I tell you a market that is growing: the organic industry. Notice how I defined that industry by lifestyle choice and not product category? A market is only growing if more people are buying from it now than they did in the past. And as people become more aware of issues around sustainability, the organic industry grows some more. So it might have started out as just food produce, through concerns over pesticides and genetically modified crops, but now we can wear organic clothing."

"So, it's important to be in a growing market?"

"Not necessarily. It's fine to be in a static market, providing you can keep growing your share of it. But if you are in a segment of a market that is growing, then as the segment grows, you can grow without doing any extra work yourself."

I thought back to the Boston matrix and my need to be in the 'star' category rather than the 'dog' category. "So, as people become even busier, more of them will want my duvet cover?"

"It's not so much about becoming busier, but wanting to spend less time doing household chores. Or wanting them to be easier. You see, I would ask yourself whether there is scope for going into the organic market yourself, using organic cotton."

"As well as the time saving thing?"

"Possibly. You see, I'm guessing you are going to have a limited range of colours and styles to begin with? If my wife is anything to go by, she will buy a duvet set to match the colours of the bedroom. So your range could be limiting if you only have three different colours. But if you position yourself in a segment that has a strong lifestyle focus, then you will sell your product on that basis, irrespective of whether it's a good colour match. Unless you are going for luminous green? Then you might have a problem selling it, regardless of which segment you appeal to!"

"Glow in the dark bedding…nice! Great, I'll think about what you've said."

"Let me give you one of our hand-outs." He handed me a small booklet. "It's something we do for our clients to help them understand this whole marketing mix concept."

"I've heard of that," I said.

"Good, because it's something you need to be aware of, but lot's of people find it quite a scary term, so we've explained it simply. However, I would like you to do something for me please. I would like you to write down a couple of sentences for each of the seven items in the mix, describing how they apply to your business."

"Alright. What should I do once I've done this?"

"Can you email it to me? Here, let me give you a business card." He handed me a beautifully designed business card. "I'm looking forward to seeing what you write."

"OK. I hope I do a good job!"

"I'm sure you will."

"Well, once I get it launched, hopefully one of my duvet sets will be a good match for your bedroom. What colour is it?"

"Good sales technique! She'd probably call it *terracotta*. I'd call it *orange*. She was inspired by a holiday we had in Sardinia a couple of years ago, so now our whole house is kind of 'earthy'."

We shook hands and left. "You handled that really well," said Uncle Steve in the car. "I was really impressed."

"Do you think? I found myself getting really cross when he kept challenging things."

"Yes, but that's his job to. It's got you thinking."

"It's got me scared, more like!"

What you've covered:

Theme	Amplification
Marketing	Understand the purpose of marketing and its importance to businesses in different situations
Marketing	The difference between *mass marketing* and *niche marketing*
Marketing	What is meant by market and product orientation

Memory hook: Orchid Marketing

Orchids provide a good hook for thinking about how we value products and markets. Orchids themselves could be a growing market, just as tulips were in the Netherlands in the 1600s (giving rise to 'tulipmania'). Perhaps they are popular because they have a unique attribute? Their uniqueness could be a lifestyle choice. If the market for orchids is growing, then all businesses in their supply chain should benefit from increased sales. However, if the market is static, then the only way to increase revenue is to take share from the competitors.

So, key points to remember:

1. Marketing is about connecting businesses and customers.
2. *Market orientation* means listening to and addressing the needs of the customer. This could be based upon lifestyle choices such as making their lives easier (easy-care fabric), or sustaining the environment (organic fabric).
3. Alternatively, *product orientation* means promoting the features of the product, striving to make it the best it can be, and assuming the market will want it.

Now ask yourself:

1. Name two products/industries that are currently in a growth phase and two others that are static.
2. What type of products might fall into the product orientation category?
3. Why are changes in advertising trends enabling niche businesses to compete with mass-market businesses?

Now ask yourself (suggested answers):

1. **Name two products/industries that are currently in a growth phase and two others that are static.**

   Growth:
   - Virtual reality technology, such as headsets, is currently in high growth.
   - Financial Technology (FinTech) - financial businesses that incorporate digital innovation are experiencing high growth.

   Static:
   - Television sales could be considered fairly static right now.
   - Milk is typically a static product. One could argue it is in slight decline as more people identify themselves with having a dairy intolerance.

2. **What type of products might fall into the product orientation category?**

   - The classic example is Henry Ford's Model T motorcar. He is renowned for having said a "customer can have a car painted any colour that he wants so long as it is black." In fact, the model T was available in other colours and his comment may have been in jest. Irrespective, car consumers nowadays are offered significantly more choice.
   - Microsoft 'Windows' was traditionally product oriented. Apple, whilst also product oriented, addressed more market needs such as simplicity, aesthetics and cyber-security.
   - Gillette has always focused on producing high quality razors and hence is heavily product oriented. Recently, companies such as Dollar Shave Club have addressed market needs by making a lower priced alternative. Unilever purchased this business for $1 billion in July 2016.

3. **Why are changes in advertising trends enabling niche businesses to compete with mass-market businesses?**

    ▪ Increasingly, more advertising is done online and around social media in particular. This provides an advantage to niche businesses since the cost is low and social media allows them to target specific segments within their niche.

    ▪ It could be argued that advertising as a means of promotion is in decline, replaced instead by indirect marketing methods such as online conversations and testimonials. There are no barriers preventing niche businesses from engaging in this kind of promotion.

CHAPTER 30

How are you positioned?

Later that evening, I took a look at the handout I'd been given on the marketing mix. On the front cover, it read 'Positioning is important...how are you positioned?' The image was of a dog lying in the shade, out of the sun.

Inside, it had seven sections each describing what were known as the 7Ps of Marketing. The first was *Product*.

Product

We can all think of a product we love, can't we? There is just something about that product that appeals to us. Perhaps it has been reliable and never let us down? Maybe it is designed in a unique way that makes us proud to own it? Possibly we have memories of where we were, when we bought it.

In a competitive world, your product or service needs to be truly special in the eyes of your key stakeholder – your customer. Your product or service needs to be loved, if you want to maximise your chances of growing your business. If it's not about being loved, then read on...

Underneath that was *Price*.

Price

Sometimes products and services can be loved on price alone. Provided it 'does what it says on the tin', we all love a bargain. All businesses need to generate sufficient income to yield a profit, so pricing your product or service at the right level is imperative. However, price is one of two variables in the income equation. The other is volume of sales. And high volume sales, gives the business more freedom to flex its price cutting muscle.

However, in some markets, a cheap price can work against you. Ask yourselves how willing your market is to paying a premium for product or service excellence. If the goal of your business is to compete at the higher price bracket, then how much is your premium going to be? Just make sure you can justify the premium and deliver a product that meets it.

Then came *Place*.

Place

Don't confuse this with where your customers live. This is not about geography – it's the one '*P*' that probably shouldn't have been a '*P*'. Place refers to your distribution channel – how your product or service reaches the end market. So maybe you sell direct to the end customer? This is known as '0 level', as there is no distribution channel. It's also referred to as 'Business to Consumer' (B2C).

Alternatively, you may sell to an intermediary, who sells it on again. This is 'Business to Business' (B2B). Having one or more intermediaries will eat into your profits compared to B2C. However, the advantage of B2B is that businesses are likely to place high volume orders. If it's a huge order, then perhaps you only need one customer?

Knowing your distribution channel affects how you market your product. Intermediaries don't need to love the product or service in the way a consumer does, but they do need to be able to sell it.

This felt a bit like reading horoscopes. Next up, *Promotion*.

Promotion

How are you going to get your product or service out there? Don't think here purely about what is easiest or cheapest for you. You might buy a really cheap advert for your product, but if it's in a magazine whose readers have little interest in what you're selling, then it's money wasted.

So where are your customers? And how cheaply can you get your message to them? Many businesses are turning to social media for this. If you go down this route, how can you get your message 'viral' in a good way? Social media for business comes with a huge warning sign: don't engage in blatant selling, as people don't like this. Give advice; give recommendations; give feedback. Then, and only then, promote. Other methods aside from social media include setting up sales teams, placing advertisements across different media, public relations (PR) and sponsorship.

Next came *People*.

People

In most cases, people are everything in a business. Few people return to a restaurant where the waiters and waitresses are rude and offensive. Finding good staff can make a business; not finding good staff can break it. Often, they need to be skilled as well as charming. Your car mechanic can be the nicest guy in the world, but if he doesn't know the oil filter from the fuel pump, then you don't want him under your customers' bonnets. If the business sells online, your team may only be responding via email or social media. They still need to be helpful, knowledgeable and good communicators though, even if they are typing in their pyjamas, on a bad hair day!

Pyjamas on a bad hair day. That sounds like my kind of job! Next was *Process*.

Process

Let's be honest, who likes telephoning a company, only to be put on hold for thirty minutes? Or going through endless menus with different options? Equally, have you ever attempted to purchase something online, only to find the website crashes near the end or won't complete your order? Process matters. The more barriers you put in to stop a customer making a purchase, or resolving a problem, the more likely you are to lose them. So get your processes right. That includes after-sales too. If something goes wrong for the customer, sort it out for them as quickly as possible. 'Word of mouth' travels far and fast.

I felt mildly told off reading that one, so promised myself to get my processes right. Last came *Physical Environment*.

Physical Environment

Business premises define a product or service. If the toilets in a restaurant are dirty, what does that say about the kitchen? If all a customer can hear is continuous announcements over the tannoy, or loud music on the radio, how is that going to make them feel? Stressed, maybe. Our physical senses matter. And that goes beyond what we see. It includes what we hear, what we smell and what we feel.

Then we need to bear in mind placement. Where you situate your business needs to be comfortable for your customers. You wouldn't expect to find a Louis Vuitton shop in a less salubrious part of town. Would their intended customers go there? And could their passers by afford to shop there?

It doesn't end there. If you sell online, the physical environment is your website or your social media pages. Are they well presented and easy to navigate?

Then came a final section.

So that's the marketing mix. It's not too bad, is it? Just remember that businesses change and evolve. So what your mix looks like now, may not be what your mix will need to be like in five years. More importantly, if your business has moved on since you started, maybe it's time to re-visit things? Here are some examples of how things might change:

Internal.

Maybe you have found a cheaper way of making the product, compared to when you started. If so, can part of this saving be passed on to the customer?
Perhaps prices need to go up?
Maybe you have brought new staff in with new expertise? Can they be leveraged to improve the product/service or create a new one?
Perhaps the management objectives have changed in a way that somehow affects your mix?

External. Remember PEST-C:

Political and legal – have the regulations around your industry changed?
Economy – is the economy within your market growing or shrinking?
Social – have people's views and attitudes changed?
Technology – have you moved with the times? Do you know what the latest innovations in your industry are?
Competition – who are you competing against and what are they doing?

It all made perfect sense, but I didn't have the first clue how to respond to Elliott's request for my interpretation. Nevertheless, I needed to get this done, so I had a stab. Here's what I came up with:

Product
My product takes the fight out of bed making. Why force a duvet into a cover when it is so much easier to place it directly on top? Not only does it save time, it makes the whole job less stressful. To save more time, our use of high quality, easy-iron cotton reduces the need to iron such a cumbersome item.

Price
Improving the design of a badly designed product should not incur a premium. We have priced our product fairly based on the cost of the materials. You will find our range matches the market price for high quality bedding, yet offers so much more.

Place
We sell direct to the end-user through our website. We consider our customer to be everyday people at home, plus hotels and guesthouses that value the time saving our design makes possible.

Promotion
We will use social media and a range of PR through newspaper features to promote the range.

People
We are a family-oriented business with strong values and a good customer service ethic.

Process
Our range can be purchased through our online store. Any problems can be resolved by telephone or email. We offer a refund policy in line with statutory rights.

Physical Environment
We are an online business with no physical premises as yet.

Potential future changes
We may consider selling our product to a limited number of retailers (B2B) in the future. However, this may require additional investment and sourcing of mass producers.
We also anticipate our design causing more established providers of duvet sets to re-think their own design.

I edited it a bit before emailing it to Elliott, copying in Uncle Steve. As it sent, a new message arrived in my Inbox. It was from 't-shirt Sam'! I reeled in horror as I read its contents.

What you've covered:

Theme	Amplification
Product	The importance of a business having the right product for its customers' needs
Price	Awareness of the different pricing strategies employed in different industries and scenarios
Promotion	Understand the various promotional strategies used by different industries and businesses
Place	Recognise that place refers to distribution channels, not geography, and explain the different options available
People	Why it's important to have good people in a business
Process	Poor processes, such as telephone answering systems, can create barriers to purchase
Physical environment	What is meant by 'physical environment' and why it's important

Memory hook: How are you positioned?

The important thing to remember here is the 7Ps are defined more in terms of how the customer relates to the purchase proposition. It's not about what works best for the business itself. Since the customer is free to decide where and who to buy from, these seven criteria help a business understand how they can influence that decision through positioning the business in the right way for their target customer.

So, key points to remember:

1. Place refers to distribution channels. Direct to consumer (B2C) is known as '0 level' as there are no intermediaries.
2. Promotion can be *above the line*, which means mass-media promotion such as TV commercials or newspaper advertisements. Alternatively, *below the line* refers to one-to-one type promotion such as email, flyers through doors or mail order catalogues.
3. Poor processes include keeping customers on-hold over the telephone and websites that consistently crash before a sale is completed.
4. If a company trades principally on low prices, then many of the other 7Ps are not considered so important. For example, the poor presentation of products and lack of packing areas in many discount supermarkets are acceptable since the low prices are the main attraction.

Now ask yourself:

1. What methods might you use to promote a theme park aimed at families?
2. What type of pricing strategies could you employ for the launch of a new virtual reality headset?

Now ask yourself (suggested answers):

1. **What methods might you use to promote a theme park aimed at families?**

   - Online videos demonstrating the rides at the park since families are likely to search the web in advance of booking tickets.
   - Offering discounted family tickets for anyone who submits an idea for a new ride – this would help create a connection and may even help create good ideas!
   - Creating an Easter egg hunt around the country with free tickets placed inside eggs – this would create awareness at springtime, which will likely be the start of the new season. Plus, children love egg hunts.
   - Working with a video game company to have the theme park featured as an ad at the start of the game or a flyer inside the packaging of the game – children play video games.

2. **What type of pricing strategies could you employ for the launch of a new virtual reality headset?**

   - **Price skimming**. This strategy involves setting a high price when the demand is high, such as at the launch stage. Since new technology products are initially price inelastic, this would be the most likely strategy for VR headsets.
   - **Penetration pricing**. This strategy involves setting prices low in order to gain market share. It would be highly unlikely for brand leaders in VR headsets to adopt this strategy, but would be preferable for budget brands that wish to disrupt the market.
   - **Dynamic pricing** would involve changing prices in line with demand, e.g. seasonality. This might occur in the run up to Christmas and could realistically be used for sale of VR headsets on retail websites such as EBay.
   - **Competitive pricing** would involve monitoring the market and setting prices to be consistent with competitors. This would only be appropriate if there were no discernible difference between headsets in terms of functionality and quality.
   - **Cost-plus pricing** is a more scientific pricing strategy of calculating the cost to produce each item (the 'cost' element) and adding on a specific profit margin (the 'plus' element).

CHAPTER 31

Street cleaner wanted: £100k per annum salary

Dear Lucinda,

I hope all is well with you? Ever since your visit with Alex, I've felt really troubled with guilt. It certainly wasn't my intention to cause problems between both of you. Alex is a lovely guy and I hope to remain friends with him. Both of you, perhaps?

However, I do need to explain something. It's true Alex and I dated a year ago and he broke my heart. As you have seen for yourself, he is very charming, intelligent and good fun to be around. The problem I had was one of trust. He seemed to always be around other girls. I'd walk into coffee shops and find him there with someone who he'd never told me about. He assured me it was just platonic or professional but I became slightly paranoid.

It became a bit of a problem for us and eventually he suggested that we break off as he was feeling 'stifled'. It hit me quite badly, as you can imagine, and as my course had come to an end, I decided to move away. That's why I came down here to start the business. We did remain friends and met up a couple of times for the day, but that was about it. He had been helping with my business idea from the start and has continued to be a good sounding board for me. To this day, I am not sure whether it was my over-sensitivity, or his way of being flirtatious and open with the opposite sex.

I just feel you needed to know and I have already told Alex that I wanted to email you. He even helped me with your email address. Hopefully what you have with Alex is different to what I had and it doesn't become a problem for you?

I wish you lots of luck with your business and if you ever need any advice or some corporate t-shirts (!) please don't hesitate to get in touch.

Yours,
Sam

I read the email a couple of times and then opened up my SMS app. I texted Alex to say I was ready to meet up and could he meet me over the weekend. I had no idea what I would be saying at the weekend, but knew I just needed to see him.

The next twenty minutes were spent lying on my bed, staring at the ceiling, waiting to hear a beep on my phone. A beep never came. Was he out dating some other naive sap like me right now? I began to get really twitchy. Then I didn't want to be alone anymore. I wanted to be with my Mum.

She was downstairs, writing something for work on the dining room table. I gave her a big hug from behind. Despite wanting to blurt out everything that had just happened, I also didn't want to hear what she might tell me. So instead, I asked her what she was doing.

"That's nice of you to ask darling. I'm actually just putting the finishing touches to my counter-proposal for work."

"So what's the plan?"

"Well I've recognised their concerns about the statistics they provided on low productivity and performance. But as a response, I've outlined the lack of employee engagement from senior management and the need to motivate staff better."

"Do you think they will like being told they are to blame though?" I was concerned Mum would antagonise the people who were deciding her fate.

"I don't think so, because I've supported it with evidence and research. It's been really interesting actually, Lu. This company called ORD International has done some research on UK businesses and found that we are really bad at engagement."

"What exactly is *engagement*?"

"I'm glad you asked! Three things, according to the Chartered Institute of Personnel and Development. It's about *intellectual engagement*, which I've taken to mean thinking deeper about how employees are feeling and why. I've given them some suggestions on how we can improve that. Then it's about *affective engagement*, which means making staff feel better about doing their job. Let's be honest, responding to housing complaints from irate tenants is hardly anyone's ideal job. And finally, providing *social engagement*. Which means we need to give them more opportunities to discuss cases and share feedback."

"But won't they say you should have been doing that anyway?" Sensing Mum's frown, I added, "don't mean to sound negative. I'm just trying to prepare you for what they may think."

"Well, I would say that we have never been empowered as middle managers to address these issues. I would take these statistics as a positive step to improving motivation within the workplace. We've always assumed that our people are just motivated by earning a wage. And we exacerbate it by offering them rewards that encourage processing ever more paperwork, when in fact that's not being very *customer centric*. Instead, if we motivated the team to spend more time calling tenants back and listening to their needs, then we would get better productivity statistics, less stage two complaints and therefore improve community satisfaction."

"So in other words, they are measuring the wrong thing?"

"Yes, our main objective is about how many forms we handle each day. That adds to the stress and boredom of the staff, hence more sickness days. And it means tenants don't feel involved and communicated with. I've read some really interesting stuff about motivation. We are still running our organisation according to the theories of this guy called Frederick Taylor, back in the 1800s! He believed people were only motivated by money and used time and motion studies to make people perform. We're doing the same thing, 150 years on!"

"That's crazy. Selling it all off to the third sector won't help, surely?"

"Not if they continue running things the same way. Although they will probably feel the same as I do."

"So what's the alternative?"

"Well after Taylor, things moved onto sociological theory through a guy called Elton Mayo. He introduced the idea that people at work should communicate more. But we need to go further and take on ideas from these people called Maslow and Herzberg."

"Where are they from?"

"No idea, but they talk about the psychological importance of work, which is exactly the problem we have."

"So, that's about getting people to love doing their job? But what if they don't?"

"It's about recognising that people work for different reasons. So, according to Maslow's Hierarchy of Needs, people go through five stages. We are currently operating at the bottom two, which are physiological and security. So basically, we are providing people with the money they need to live and the security of work. Except, we need to realise that most people need more from their work than that. So the third component is social. But the fourth is the need for esteem, which means people need to feel recognised and empowered."

"And the fifth?"

Mum looked back at her notes. "The fifth is called self-actualisation. I think that is about fulfilling potential. I guess this is for those people who treat their work as a career, rather than simply a job."

"So, are you going to propose that your team moves towards providing more opportunities for progression?"

"Not just my team, but the whole organisation. I think other areas should be doing more of this. I think our whole Human Resource objectives need a good shake up. It's the same with Herzberg. He talks about motivator factors such as increased recognition and responsibility over hygiene factors like working conditions and wage levels."

"Sorry Mum, but I don't agree with that. I mean, working conditions and salary are really important things to pretty much everyone."

"Yes, they are if they're not there, but they don't motivate people. So he's not saying people will accept low pay and a rubbish work environment. People will be dissatisfied if they don't get them. But they are not the factors that have the potential to satisfy. For that, you need to look at ways of making people feel valued in their job. So, I could be paid £100,000 a year to clean the streets. But it's not going to make me love the job."

"I think I could love that job for £100,000 a year!"

"I'd love you for that too, Lu! But after a while, being your Mum would kick in and I'd have to get you off those streets."

"So it's going to need changing the way your team approaches their job then?"

"Yes, it is. I'm suggesting we re-write the job descriptions and build more of this into their day-to-day activities. Instead of recognising them for the number of forms they process, we appraise them on doing the right thing and getting tenants the solution they need. So move towards non-financial methods of motivation."

"At the end of the day, isn't this all about cutting council costs though? I don't see how motivating staff will do that."

"I'm suggesting there are efficiency savings we can make without losing staff. Plus, improving our community engagement will raise our profile within the public sector. Not all metrics should be financial."

"God, I hope it works Mum."

"Me too. What I'm suggesting actually gets them the results they want, which is more productivity and more satisfied tenants. The last thing I'm adding is a timescale of one year, by which time they will see the outputs they're looking for. So I'm hoping that will help swing it. Anyway, how are you?"

"Compared to this Mum, my problems are nothing. I'm just a bit confused with Alex, that's all."

"It must be hard darling, but you've only known each other for a few weeks. My advice would be to just see how things go. I know it's not the advice I'd have wanted when I was your age, but it is right thing to do."

"I know, you're right. Don't worry, I won't let it get to me."

"Good. And did everything go alright with that man Uncle Steve introduced you too?"

"Elliott? Yes, he's got me thinking about things in a slightly different way."

"Marketing people have a habit of doing that!"

My phone beeped. Alex? No, it was the very man we were talking about. He'd received my response on the marketing mix.

"Mum, you're not going to believe this. Elliott's just offered me a job!"

What you've covered:

Theme	Amplification
Motivation	Motivation theories such as Taylor, Mayo, Maslow and Herzberg
Motivation	The importance of motivation within business
Engagement	What do we mean by 'workforce engagement'
Motivation	Which non-financial methods of motivation are used today

Memory hook: Street cleaner wanted: £100k per annum salary

Lucinda and her Mum discuss the merits of being paid £100,000 per year to perform a difficult job. This hooks nicely onto the arguments around using money as a motivating factor for work. Other methods of motivating a workforce are then discussed, as per the discussion questions below.

So, key points to remember:

1. A motivated workforce is more likely to perform better.
2. F.W. Taylor believed that people were only motivated by money and used scientific techniques to measure his workers' performance.
3. Elton Mayo studied and advocated the social benefits of work.
4. Maslow and Herzberg studied the psychological impacts of work. Their theories advocated use of motivator factors (e.g. recognition & responsibility) over hygiene factors (pay & working conditions).
5. During an organisational restructure, employees whose jobs are at risk are invited to submit counter proposals outlining an alternative way to achieve the same objectives that avoid job redundancy.
6. One disadvantage to outsourcing work is the people who then perform that job don't understand the culture or role significance in the same way that the internally employed staff would have done.

Now ask yourself:

1. Which financial methods of motivation are used in business today?
2. Describe some non-financial methods of motivation that are used?

Now ask yourself (suggested answers):

1. **Which financial methods of motivation are used in business today?**

   - **Wage/Salary** is the most common form of financial incentive. Employees are paid a set amount each week/month. At certain review periods, employees may have a salary rise if performance has been good. The employee benefit to salaries is the security of knowing that amount will be paid. The downside is it can create a limiting effect on effort since the salary is capped. Wages are typically for lower level workers and are paid weekly, whereas salaries are paid monthly.
   - **Commission** is paid to employees as a percentage of whatever income they generate for the business. It is most commonly used in sales jobs. So, whilst the financial security is low, opportunity is high. Few employees are willing to work on a total commission system, so a common halfway house is a basic salary plus commission model.
   - **Bonus** payments address the capping of salaries by offering employees an additional amount based on performance. Many executives and senior managers receive bonus payments. They are an example of performance related pay (PRP).
   - **Piece rate**. Common in manufacturing, employees are paid on the basis of the number of units they produce. This has the benefit of linking pay to output, but can cause employees to rush work or cut corners in order to get more completed.
   - **Profit sharing** and **share ownership** are more PRP systems that reward employees for good performance. However, in most cases these will be offered across the organisation, so are less focused on individual performance.

2. **Describe some non-financial methods of motivation that are used?**

   - **Job design** enables HR managers to construct jobs in a way that make them more interesting, varied and challenging. This can be a very powerful non-financial technique since it aims to make employees enjoy their work more. Job design could comprise of a number of approaches, such as:

- o **Job enlargement** - growing the context of the job to a wider range of functions;
- o **Job rotation** - allowing workers to vary the tasks they do during the day/week;
- o **Job enrichment** - making the job more challenging and less repetitive.

- **Team working** is used to enable employees to work in larger units, rather than in isolation. The aim is to increase camaraderie and the social aspect of work, in order to increase motivation and satisfaction.

- **Flexible working** aims to support employees find a more appropriate work/life balance. It can include working varied hours and days, as well as working from home.

- **Empowerment** is a technique for enabling employees to take more control of decision-making within the workplace. The goal is to make them feel more included and valued.

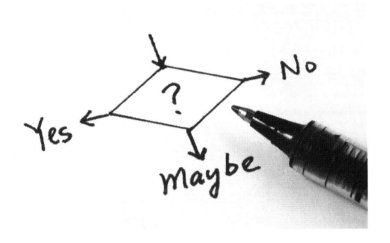

I was sat with Uncle Steve in his favourite pub. I was telling him about the job offer from Elliott.

"Sounds like you have a tough decision to make, Lulu."

"I know! It's only an internship for three months, but he's pretty much said it will turn into a full-time trainee marketer job from September."

"Well, you'd have to pass the interview, but of course, he'd be mad not to choose you!"

"But where does that leave *Duvet Days*?"

"That's very much up to you. You could ask for the job part-time, so you'd have some time in the week to build it up. Or you could just do it in your evenings and weekends. Or. And this is a big 'or'. You could see if he wants to take a share of the business?"

"Why would he want to do that? And why would I want to let him? If Elliott came in too, that would dilute the share even more."

"Yes, but just think of all the experience and contacts he has. He should be able to promote it in a way we couldn't. Sometimes, you have to give a little, to receive a lot."

"I'm not sure, Uncle Steve."

"It's just another option, Lulu. At the end of the day, business is all about decision-making. And sometimes you have to take an option that is more for the long-term than the short-term. A strategic decision they would call it in that Business School of your friend. I'm pretty sure that giving it up is not an option, right?"

"Definitely not. I won't give it up."

"I didn't think so. So let's draw it as a decision." He took out his notebook and drew a diagram. "That's called a decision tree."

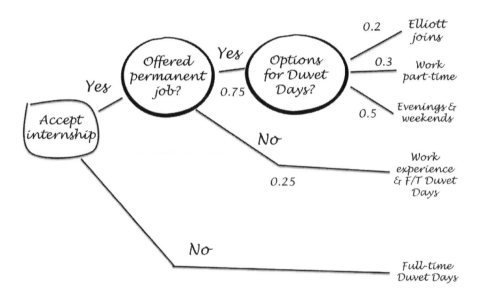

I studied it hard. "So, the first option is to accept the internship or not?"

"That's right. And because it's a decision, it's shaped as a square. If you don't accept it, you carry on with *Duvet Days* as normal. If you do accept it, then you have an uncertainty about whether you get offered the job permanently. Uncertainties are shaped as a circle."

"So if I get the job permanently, it leads to a further question mark over what I do with *Duvet Days*? You've drawn it as an uncertainty, but isn't it a decision?"

"I wouldn't say so, because neither Elliott joining, or offering you the job part-time, are within your control. Of course, if he were to volunteer, then it would lead to a decision for you. So if Elliott joined the company, his team might help you run it and you could work full-time. Or you can ask for agreement to only work part-time, which he may be unlikely to agree to. Or you can work full-time and try to run the business in evenings and weekends."

"Whoa, information overload! There are too many decisions and uncertainties here to make sense of!"

"Which is why decision trees come in useful. They help you see the wood from the trees!"

"So, what are these numbers: 0.75 and 0.25?"

"You have to assign probabilities to every uncertainty since you don't know what is going to happen. So I have said there is a 75% chance you will get offered a permanent job, and a 25% chance you won't. All outcomes must sum to 100%, obviously."

"OK. But how does it help me decide what to do?"

"Well it doesn't. To finish it off we would need to assign values to each of these outcomes on the right. So values could be in monetary terms or they could be some measure of your happiness. You then multiply each value by the probability of it occurring. And the path that provides the highest value is the optimal path and the one you should follow."

"Shouldn't I just do what seems right to me? You know – go with my gut instinct?"

"Ah, make a decision based on intuition? Yes, you could. But when decisions become quite complex, it's better to be more scientific about it."

"So, do you use these pointless decision trees much, then?"

"They're not quite so pointless! And yes, I use them quite a lot. Take this one, for example." He showed me one on an earlier page.

"These are the options for your own business?"

"Exactly. So option one is to buy my competitor out. Option two is reject the offer and carry on as we are. Option three is look to grow the business in other ways."

"So, why not just grow the business? That sounds like the safest option?"

"But growing the business would still need more investment to make it a bigger company. If we invest in it ourselves, that would mean taking on more financial risk."

"In what way?"

"Well, the business has some retained profits. In other words, over the years where we have made a profit, we've saved some away. But that's probably not enough to do what needs to be done, like taking on extra sales staff or moving to bigger premises. Which means your Aunt Kath and I would need to invest more of our money in it. Alternatively, we could sell some of the company assets, but we don't have many assets that we don't need. Those options are known as internal sources of finance. Another approach is external finance."

"Like, borrow money from the bank?"

"Yes that's one option. Another is to offer some of the business in exchange for finance from either venture capital, or sell shares publicly on the stock exchange. But we're not big enough for that. However, as it happens, I know someone who wants to invest £500,000 in the company."

"Oh my God, that's amazing!"

"Well, not so amazing. He's done it because he wants me to relocate it to London."

"So you'll move to London? And why does he want to invest?"

"No, we wouldn't move, although most of my week would probably be spent there. Why invest? I suppose he can see the value in what we do. He reckons there is nobody in London doing what we do, which I don't quite believe. But if he wants to keep polishing my ego, who am I to stop him?!"

"I'm completely lost on where that fits in on the decision tree."

"OK. £500,000 represents around 50% of our share capital. Which basically means he would have a stake in about one third of the business. So, do I want to give away that much share of the business?"

"Shouldn't you just go with your gut instinct?"

"Not really. For something like this, I need to know what is the right thing to do financially, before we decide emotionally. And for that, I need to calculate everything out."

"So, how big a company could you become if you accepted his offer?"

"Aha! That's the great unknown. He's predicting we would become a ten million pound annual turnover business."

"Ten million! A year?!"

"That's what he's predicting. Which, based on our usual 10% operating profit margin, would work out at a whopping one million a year in pre-tax profit."

"So, you'd effectively be too rich for this pub. You wouldn't want to be seen with me, Mum and Jake anymore. Oh and you'd probably trade in Aunt Kath for a twenty year old model."

"No to the first two, but the last one sounds like a plan!"

"Yeah right, in your dreams."

"Well you suggested it!"

"Anyway, coming back to reality, what the hell are you going to do? Do you have to give him that much of the business?"

"Good question. He doesn't want to be a shareholder. He just sees it purely as an investment. So it would be loan capital, not share capital. But I'm still not comfortable with a gearing ratio of 33%."

"Gearing. What's gearing?"

"So, currently my business is funded entirely by shareholder capital – which is basically me and your Aunt. Gearing is the ratio of loan capital to share capital. So if the amount of loan capital is low, that would mean our gearing is low. Or we could receive more loan capital, like the 33%, but in return for a greater share of the business. That's high gearing."

"What a huge decision, Uncle Steve!"

"I know, scary stuff, eh? It's actually not the first time I've been approached by this guy about moving it to London. The location of a business is so important and whilst the opportunities over here are good, there are lots more down there and the fees basically double overnight."

"But why can't you have the London clients, with their double fees, but still be based over here?"

"Most of our clients are based around London anyway. It's just having a base there, opens more doors, I guess."

"So why not do it?"

"Well, when you create a business, it becomes more than just about you. At least, it is if you have ethics. So I've got my team up here. What would I do with them? I'm not sure it's work you can do remotely. I know the families of the people I've employed. I don't want to do something that damages them. Stuff like that."

"But isn't business all about making the right decision for you?"

"It is to some. In its simplest form, the purpose of an organisation is to maximise shareholder wealth. So yeah, to those who are just in it for the money, it would be a no brainer."

"And for others?"

"For others, things are a bit different. Business is also about delivering on its social conscience. We have decisions that are more than about money. Don't get me wrong; shareholder wealth still matters too. But, particularly with smaller companies like mine, sometimes you have to do the right thing for reasons other than making more money. Corporate social responsibility they call it."

"But you can still be socially responsible and make money, Uncle Steve."

"Yes I know. But there are other stakeholders in this. I guess it all boils down to whether it is all about the money. And for your Aunt and me, it's never all been about the money. But then, we're not getting any younger and we need to start thinking about our future. I don't fancy working into my seventies, thank you very much. You will have to, but not me!"

"Me neither! I want to be living on my yacht, sailing around the Caribbean!"

"Well then, you'd better make the right decision on that internship."

"Which is?"

"Buggered if I know, Lulu. I can't even decide whether to go to London or not! Come on, let's head back."

As we were walking back, my phone beeped. It was a text from Alex asking me to meet him for coffee tomorrow. I said yes. At least that's one decision I didn't need a tree for.

What you've covered:

Theme	Amplification
Decision-making	How decision trees are constructed and what their benefits are
Decision-making	The difference between scientific decision-making and intuitive decision-making
Business finance	The different ways a business can be financed, specifically internal versus external sources
Business location	Some of the consequences of relocating a business, such as personal circumstances and implications for employees
Ethics	The meaning of ethics in business and the term 'corporate social responsibility'

Memory hook: Decisions, decisions

Decision-trees are one of several scientific tools to help evaluate different decision options. Other tools include critical path analysis and cost-benefit analysis. The alternative is to go with gut instinct (intuitive decision-making). This chapter also highlights how decisions affect a variety of different stakeholders, including: employees, customers, shareholders and investors.

So, key points to remember:

1. Intuitive decisions (i.e. gut instinct) involve making what seems to instinctively be the right choice. Scientific methods include tools like decision-trees that use numerical analysis.
2. Within decision-making, there is a distinction between decisions and uncertainties. Decisions are entirely within the decision-makers control. Uncertainties are outside of their control, but can be measured using probabilities.
3. Ownership of a business breaks down into share capital, which is owned by shareholders and loan capital, which is money invested through external sources.
4. Gearing refers to the ratio between the two. Highly geared companies have a high proportion of loan capital.
5. Corporate Social Responsibility means respecting the organisation's obligations to society and the wider environment. An organisation with good ethics will think about the impacts of its decisions on others before making them and communicate clearly what they are doing and why.

Now ask yourself:

1. What are the distinctions between strategic, tactical and operational decisions in the context of Disney's decision to create a theme park in Europe (Disneyland Paris)?
2. What happens to profit in a limited company at the end of a financial year and what factors go into the decision on how to apportion it?
3. What is meant by investment appraisal and what are the three different options?

Now ask yourself (suggested answers):

1. **What are the distinctions between strategic, tactical and operational decisions in the context of Disney's decision to create a theme park in Europe (Disneyland Paris)?**

    - The **strategic** decisions were whether to create one at all and if so, where to situate it. For example, a number of sites were considered, but the final alternatives were Spain and France. Strategic decisions are: made for the long-term, highly important and difficult to reverse. People at the top of the organisation typically make the strategic decisions.
    - **Tactical** decisions are greater in number, will be more short-term, and will be less significant. In Disney's case, decisions such as what type of rides to build, which sponsors to work with and pricing models for food and beverages would be tactical decisions. Senior managers within the organisation will make them.
    - **Operational** decisions are typically made once the tactics are in place. They are lower level, made frequently and typically made my middle management within different departments. Examples for Disney include: hiring staff, selecting catering suppliers and park maintenance decisions.

2. **What happens to profit in a limited company at the end of a financial year and what factors go into the decision on how to apportion it?**

    The shareholders will decide how to allocate the profit between retaining it within the business and distributing as a dividend. If the shareholders feel the business needs to retain more cash, then they will distribute a smaller dividend.

    In private limited companies, the shareholders are likely to be just the directors. They will have anticipated receiving a certain dividend as income and so are likely to issue dividends at a similar level to the past.

    For public limited companies however, external shareholders respond positively to receiving dividends. So, issuing a large dividend pleases them and also sends out a positive message of confidence for other potential investors.

3. **What is meant by investment appraisal and what are the three different options?**

Investment appraisal involves evaluating the likely financial return from an investment. Its purpose is to assist the investor in deciding whether to pursue an investment, or not. A number of methods are used, however the most common are:

- **Average rate of return** – adding together the expected annual cash flows for each year the investment will be active and dividing it by the number of years. This is the most basic method.
- **Discounted cash flow techniques** (such as 'net present value') that take account of the future value of money invested today. For example, the real value of £10,000 today is likely to be more than the real value of £10,000 in twenty years time.
- **Payback period** is an evaluation of the time required to recover the cost of the investment (typically in years). An investor will likely decline the opportunity if the time to return the capital is too great or if an alternative opportunity could yield a faster payback.

CHAPTER 33

Black Magic

We embraced briefly and unnaturally outside of the coffee shop and then Alex bought us our 'usuals'. The place was fairly empty, which made things slightly awkward as it felt like our every word was being broadcast across the shop.

"How is the business coming on?" asked Alex.

"It's good," I replied with an air of relief that we were breaking the ice. "I'm thinking of calling it *Duvet Days*. Oh, and I met a marketing guru last week and he's offered me an internship for three months."

"Hey, that's excellent! What's his name?"

"He's called Elliott Black."

"OK, I've met him once. He's meant to be very good. His business used to be called 'Black Magic', but it wasn't going down very well. I think he was getting all sorts of strange phone calls. So he changed it to something about orchids I think."

"Yes, he's got them everywhere. Black Magic? That's hilarious! You would think a marketing expert would know not to call a business something like that."

"Well, it certainly caught the eye. It got him very well known, but not necessarily for the right reasons. Anyway, you should take the internship offer. It will be good experience for you."

"How's things with you?" I asked, not wanting to acknowledge his advice.

"They're alright, I guess." A long pause followed by a large slurp of coffee each, almost preparing us for the inevitable conversation ahead. "Look, I'm really sorry about putting you in that situation a couple of weeks back. It was insensitive and stupid."

"Well, yes. But then, you're a bloke, so it comes with the territory!" We both laughed nervously. "You know I had an email from her?" I couldn't quite say her name and I didn't want to call her 't-shirt Sam' as that would come across as bitchy.

"Yes, she texted me to say she wanted to contact you."

"What I'm confused about Alex, is whether you see me as just another in a long line of conquests. She suggested you were a perpetual flirt."

"Honestly, that's not the case! I can't tell you how much that's not the case. What Sam has told you is her version of events. And I can see how from her perspective it looked like that. But the truth is she has real trust issues that lead her to distort reality. So, what she probably didn't tell you is that the woman she saw me having coffee with is actually my step-sister. And the other people I spoke to were just on my course. I was completing my degree at the time."

"Your step-sister? Why didn't she know you had a step-sister and why didn't you introduce her?"

"I tried, but she just ran out when she saw us together. She did know I had a step-sister, but I didn't tell her I was meeting her, so she had no expectation of it being her."

"Why didn't you tell her?"

"Amy…that's my step-sister, just texted me out of the blue and said she was down the road and did I fancy getting out of the library for an hour. I wasn't going to text Sam and let her know something as trivial as that. What became worrying was that Sam had a habit of turning up wherever I was. At first it seemed coincidence, but then it became a bit obvious. I felt like I was being stalked by my own girlfriend."

"Right." I tried to gather my thoughts. "So, I can give you the benefit of the doubt on that. It does seem like she's a bit of a fruitcake. A very attractive fruitcake, which is a bit annoying! But what I don't understand is…" I tried to find the right words. "Well, if you went through all of this with her, why within a few weeks of meeting me, did you decide to introduce me to her? I mean, if she's as nuts as she appears, surely you wouldn't want to see her again yourself, let alone bring your new 'girlfriend' and her together?" I became aware that I signed two inverted commas with my fingers when saying girlfriend. It was one of my pet hates and now I was doing it!

"Yes, I know it was really foolish. The truth is we had stayed in touch as friends and she later admitted to having trust issues and took full responsibility for what happened. So I decided that it would be fine to introduce you to her. She told me she had a boyfriend, so I didn't expect what happened to actually happen. I realise now it was a big mistake."

"Yeah, pretty big. But can you see that from where I'm sat, it looked like you were almost showing off to me? Like she is your trophy ex-girlfriend?"

"It wasn't meant to be that at all. I don't see her as being a trophy. I see you as much more attractive, if you want to know the truth. So if there was any showing off, it would have been you to her."

"Well, that kind of makes me feel better, but then doesn't at the same time. Because if I take that literally, you were using me to try and make her jealous?"

"No, no, sorry that came out all wrong! I wasn't showing off anyone, I was just trying to help you with your business."

"But you've already introduced me to lots of people, like that hoverboard guy. Why did you need to introduce me to her? We had to take a two hour train journey just to see her."

"I know, I know. But I just thought that because she was in the textile industry, it might help. Look, if I could turn back the clock, we would never have gone there. I can't, but I'm also not the bad person you probably think I am."

"I sort of believe you. And I really want to. But it's just still a bit weird for me to process. At least I agreed to meet you though. That's a good sign. And I haven't poured this vanilla latte over your head. Yet!"

"You can, if it would make you feel better."

"Nah, that would be a waste of a good latte."

"Look, I've got something to ask you. And you can say no. There's a trip to Prague coming up. It's part of the government's European trade mission. We can take three business owners with us, all expenses paid. We had filled the three spots, but then one guy dropped out at the last minute. So, I was wondering if you would like to come in his place? We'd just be there as 'associates', I promise."

"Associates. Blimey Alex, you are a strange one. After all we've talked about, you now want me to come on a trip with you! Who are the other two? International supermodels?"

He laughed, until he could see I wasn't joking. "One is making this dog kennel product and needs a manufacturer. The other has got a hotel website idea."

"You didn't need to justify it, I didn't really think you'd be bringing supermodels. It sounds good, but I just think it's too soon. And to be honest, please don't take this the wrong way. But ever since we've met, I'm struggling to think of one date we've been on that doesn't involve your business friends." I paused to think. "Oh, hang on, we went to the cinema. Sorry, one date. But even that was to see 'The Wolf of Wall Street'!"

"Hey, you chose that! Going to the comedy night was meant to be just a fun night out. And all the others, well yes I guess so. But I was trying to help. Really."

"But now you're wanting to take me to Prague and you haven't even met my Mum yet. I haven't met your parents. I haven't met your step-sister. It's all a bit too soon."

"You can trust me you know. I would look after you, and it would be purely professional. Separate rooms and stuff."

"Yes, definitely separate rooms! I know, and it does sound lovely. But I'm just not sure. Let me think about it. When is this happening anyway? Tomorrow probably, knowing you!"

"It's in two weeks."

"Two weeks! But I've got college and stuff. Really, I think you should invite someone else. What about hoverboard man?"

"No, I don't think he wants anything in Prague. And besides, he's a bit irritating after more than thirty minutes."

"Thirty minutes? Try five. Just kidding. Anyway, what am I going to get out of Prague? Besides you knocking on my door at two in the morning?"

He smiled. "I'd be the perfect gentleman and you know it. There is this textile manufacturer out there that's meant to be doing something innovative. I thought you could meet them. Anyway, it's only for three days. I'd have to go to the meetings with the other two, but for the rest of the time, we could just chill out."

"Mmm."

"Just think about it. I have until next Wednesday to finalise things. And until then, you can invite me around to meet your Mum."

"My Mum would definitely pour coffee over your head!" He looked aghast. "I'm just kidding. She might be a bit frosty at first, but I'm sure you'd win her around with your usual charm."

"Well, I hope so."

"Look, I've got to go," I said. "I need to go and see someone about something, But I'm glad we've cleared the air and I will give you the benefit of the doubt about t-shirt Sam."

"T-shirt Sam?"

"Yes sorry, it's a nickname my friend Lucy christened her. After what I've heard today, I'd say she's got away lightly with that."

"Has she got a nickname for me?"

"Lucy? You don't want to know what she calls you right now!"

"Oh great, everyone hates me!"

"Well, that's The Sisterhood for you. Treat us nice and we'll be fine. My little brother doesn't hate you."

"How old is he?"

"Thirteen. To be honest, he doesn't even know about you. But if he did, he wouldn't hate you. Unless you support Liverpool."

"I don't do football."

"That's the best answer you've said yet!"

We embraced outside the coffee shop and he went to give me a kiss. I offered him my cheek. And then patted his bum.

What you've covered:

Theme	Amplification
Branding	The importance of selecting a strong and appropriate brand name for a business
Globalisation	The trade of goods and services across the world
International business	The meaning of 'import' and 'export' and the value both can bring to a country's economy

Memory hook: Black Magic

Black Magic is a good example of a brand name that conveys the wrong impression of a business. Whilst it might have been a good name for dark chocolates, it doesn't work so well for a marketing consultancy. Globalisation potentially exacerbates brand name confusion and potential embarrassment, since the meaning of words in different countries is often very different.

So, key points to remember:

1. The UK government provides a number of overseas trade missions for businesses to make import/export connections in other countries. It is in their interests to do this, since it helps grow UK sales and develops international relations.
2. Purchasing goods from overseas is known as import; selling goods overseas is export.
3. Ease of worldwide travel and online communication has been two key drivers of globalisation over the last century. However, trade has been conducted internationally for thousands of years.

Now ask yourself:

1. Do you know of any major brands that changed their name?
2. What feature do successful brand names typically have in common?

Now ask yourself (suggested answers):

1. **Do you know of any major brands that changed their name?**

    - Google was initially called Backrub.
    - Brad's Drink was changed to Pepsi-Cola.
    - Norwich Union changed its name to Aviva.

2. **What feature do successful brand names typically have in common?**

    If you think about it, brand names are usually single words. Those that comprise of multiple words are often shortened to one word, e.g. Marks & Spencer to 'M&S'; Mercedes-Benz to 'Mercedes' (or even 'Merc') and Proctor & Gamble to 'P&G'. The shorter the word, the easier it is to remember and say.

CHAPTER 34

Vanity, sanity, reality

My next meeting with Uncle Steve was around at their house. He wanted us to talk budgets so we could start developing a business plan.

"So, how does this differ from the profit forecast you showed me?" I asked.

"That helped us understand how the business should perform after the first year. Ideally, we would need to extend this to three or even five years. It also helped us to plan things like how much you could afford to take out as a salary. But it's more about the long term or 'bigger picture'. A budget will help you to figure out how you need to control the business on a month to month basis."

"But isn't it going to be really difficult to know how much we can sell each month until we start?"

"What happens in reality may be different from what we budget for, yes. But having the budget in place will help us to see where we need to be getting to each month, so we can see how good or bad things are. Then we can take the necessary action. Plus, remember we also need to know how much to invest at the start. A budget will help massively with that. Some businesses that are highly seasonal have periods in the year when they sell lots and then other times when they sell nothing. Whilst that shouldn't apply hugely to us, we might expect to receive a sales boost in the run up to Christmas."

"And this budget will go into the business plan?"

"Absolutely. Here, I've drafted something for you. Take a look." He handed me a spreadsheet that he had printed out.

	Sep	Oct	Nov	Dec	Jan	Feb	Mar	Apr	May	Jun	July	Aug	Total
Sales: single	360	450	585	585	450	495	585	720	855	855	720	540	7,200
Sales: double	880	1,045	1,375	1,375	1,045	1,210	1,375	1,760	2,090	2,200	1,760	1,375	17,490
Sales: king	480	600	780	780	600	660	780	960	1,140	1,140	960	720	9,600
Total sales	**1,720**	**2,095**	**2,740**	**2,740**	**2,095**	**2,365**	**2,740**	**3,440**	**4,085**	**4,195**	**3,440**	**2,635**	**34,290**
Materials	436	531	695	695	531	600	695	872	1,036	1,064	872	668	8,692
Labour	296	361	472	472	361	407	472	592	703	722	592	454	5,901
Delivery	32	39	51	51	39	44	51	64	76	78	64	49	638
Total cost of sales	**764**	**931**	**1,217**	**1,217**	**931**	**1,051**	**1,217**	**1,528**	**1,815**	**1,864**	**1,528**	**1,171**	**15,231**
Salaries	813	813	813	813	813	813	813	813	813	813	813	813	9,750
Building costs	100	100	100	100	100	100	100	100	100	100	100	100	1,200
Marketing	750	750	750	600	250	250	300	300	350	350	250	100	5,000
Other costs	1,048	48	48	48	48	48	48	48	48	48	48	48	1,580
Total indirect costs	**2,711**	**1,711**	**1,711**	**1,561**	**1,211**	**1,211**	**1,261**	**1,261**	**1,311**	**1,311**	**1,211**	**1,061**	**17,530**
Profit/loss	**-1,755**	**-546**	**-188**	**-38**	**-46**	**104**	**262**	**651**	**960**	**1,021**	**701**	**404**	**1,529**

"So, it starts with sales?" I asked. "Which is another word for revenue? Or turnover? Agh, it's so confusing!"

"Don't worry – they all mean the same thing. 'Unit sales' are the physical number we sell. So we might sell ten per month. But 'sales' can also refer to the money those unit sales has generated – this is sales revenue. Turnover is the term for the revenue generated over a full year. For example, we could say that *Duvet Days* will be a 'thirty four thousand turnover business'."

"Right, that makes more sense."

"You always start a budget by calculating sales revenue, because it needs to be an honest account of what is possible. If you try and fit your sales projections to your anticipated costs, then it might balance, but could be totally unrealistic."

"So I could decide I need a £50,000 salary? And then I engineer the revenue to achieve that, even though it probably wouldn't happen?"

"Exactly. And then a year down the line, you go bust."

I studied the table for ages. It looked quite complicated, but once you figured it out, it wasn't too bad. Then I noticed a few things.

"Why is the marketing cost so different every month?"

"Well, think about it. You are going to need to spend more on marketing at the beginning, in order to get the product noticed. Then you will also probably want to promote heavily in the run up to Christmas. But then people don't spend much in the early part of the year, so it will tail off. Gradually it builds back up until the summer, where people are not thinking so much about duvet covers and more about the beach."

"I see. But all other costs stay the same, except for 'other costs', which is really high in the first month?"

"That's right. I've put the initial set-up costs into September, although they might need to be spent before then."

"And this totally matches with our profit forecast?"

"It should do, yes. Otherwise we are forecasting one thing and budgeting for something else. Do you see the importance of budgeting now?"

"Yes, I definitely get it! Thanks, Uncle Steve." I looked again. "Hang on, we don't start to make a monthly profit until February! Isn't that really bad?"

"That's the problem most start-up companies have. It's hard to make a new business profitable. So you remember I said we need to know how much to invest at the start? Well this budget tells us that we are not going to break even for at least the first five months. So as an investor, you need me to inject some capital into the business that will easily cover the losses in those first five months. It's known as 'working capital'; the money we need to operate the business on a day-to-day basis. I think £5,000 should cover it."

"That's great, Uncle Steve. Thanks so much!"

"Not at all, you can buy me a Porsche after your first million! In fact, we're doing well to even be in that position after only five months. Some companies wait years before they start to balance the books."

"How do they survive?"

"Well, often they don't. Take Google and Amazon. Stock market investors have basically been financing them for years, even though they lost loads of money in the first few years. Who knows, if they had fallen way short on their forecasts at any time, the investors might have got nervous and bailed out. Then they wouldn't exist today. It's hard to imagine a world without Google and Amazon now, but it could have happened, and may still do one day. Pretty scary stuff, if you have billions of dollars invested in you. Luckily, I don't have that much money!"

"I'm sure you do. It's just all hidden under the mattress!"

"Ha, I wish! Now, once the business is up and running, you will need to regularly update this with the actual cash in and cash out. This will generate the all important *variances*."

"Variances. And they are…?"

"A variance is the difference between what we budgeted for and what actually happened. So a variance can be adverse if we've not done as well as expected. Or it can be favourable, if we have. We need to make sure most, or even all, of our variances are favourable."

"So, if I overspend on marketing, that would create an adverse variance?"

"Yes, so look. In year one, we have budgeted for a total marketing spend of £5,000. After three months, which is the first quarter, you should have spent three lots of £750 … which comes to … £2,250. Now, let's say you went crazy and actually spent £3,750 in those three months. So you would have a whopping adverse marketing variance of £1,500 at that stage. This would mean you'd need to significantly reduce your marketing spend for the remainder of the year, in order to keep to budget."

"But what if the marketing is going really well and we are selling loads more items than we expected? It would be stupid to stop spending on something that is working, just because we need to keep to budget."

"Good point, Lulu. So you would look at your sales revenue variance first. If you were way up on your sales, then yes, it would be fine to overspend on marketing. The only problem could be if these additional sales are putting pressure on the operational side of the business. So, if we didn't expect to sell this many items, maybe the machinists we're using are unable to cope? That means the business is growing too fast. It's a nice problem to have, but some businesses encounter cash flow problems if they grow too rapidly. It's known as *overtrading*."

"How can doing too well be a problem?!"

"Well, it's usually about pushing the finances too fast, too quickly. But in our case, what if the machinists being overrun means that quality suffers? Perhaps we start letting customers down? It's unlikely, but it can happen. So we would either cut back on marketing to control our sales. Or we expand the business faster than we anticipated. Employ more machinists. Maybe even look to mass produce."

"But without updating the budget, we wouldn't know the situation. I get it."

"Good. Now in the final spreadsheet, this will appear as a cash flow budget."

"How is cash different from profit?"

"It can be massive, Lulu. Some businesses can be highly profitable, yet still have no cash in the bank."

"How is that possible?"

"Well, when a company sells something, particularly those who are B2B, it doesn't always receive that money straight away. But it's still counted as a sale, because they'll have generated an invoice. So the profit might look good. However, the company will probably have already spent money on things like materials, manufacturing and staff. So they'll have no money in the bank to show for that sale."

"That's crazy! Why would businesses operate like that?"

"It's known as trade credit – giving customers time to pay. And it's a common reason why businesses struggle financially. A business owned by a good friend of mine went bust because he kept allowing his customers to exceed their credit limits. The norm is 30 days, but he was letting people go 60, even 90 days. Of course, when other businesses heard about his great credit facilities, they were buying from him too. So he thought he was doing really well. Then the recession came along and they couldn't pay him. Some of them went bust and eventually he went down with them. Sales that customers can't repay are known as *bad debts*. His were so bad the bank pulled the rug from under him."

"That's awful! Is he alright now?"

"A bit battered and bruised, but yes. He's found a job as an engineer. Of course, businesses could negotiate trade credit for their own purchases too. But if they're a new business, or are buying from other small companies, they're unlikely to get it."

"But won't we be receiving the money as soon as someone purchases a duvet cover?"

"Yes, and that's why our business model is a good one. We don't pay lots of money in advance for stock and we get paid more or less as soon as someone buys from us. There'll be a couple of days waiting for the transactions to be processed, but that's fine."

"I'll take this away then," I said, holding up the piece of paper. "Can you send it to me by email as well, please?"

"Of course. Have a good look at it because you need to make sure you agree. Otherwise, we'll end up with cash flow problems of our own. Right, I know your Aunt wants a catch up on your girly stuff, so you should go and see her. I've got a conference call with this guy from London in about thirty minutes."

I told Aunt Kath about Prague over two mugs of hot chocolate. She thought I should accept the offer. She said she'd have loved to be invited to Prague when she was my age. But the furthest Uncle Steve took her was Bognor Regis. So later that evening, I accepted!

What you've covered:

Theme	Amplification
Budgets	The reason why budgets are set and how they differ from financial statements (i.e. Profit and Loss account)
Trade credit	The meaning of trade credit and the risks it can create for businesses
Sales definitions	The distinction between unit sales, sales revenue and turnover
Cash flow	Why cash flow matters and the ways in which a business can experience cash flow problems
Variances	The use of variances within a budget

Memory hook: Vanity, sanity, reality

In this important chapter, this phrase is used to distinguish between revenue (vanity), profit (sanity) and cash (reality). Uncle Steve explains the importance of budgeting for a business. They also discuss the use of variances to show where performance has been good (favourable) and not so good (adverse).

So, key points to remember:

1. Budgets are about financial performance throughout the year. Financial statements, such as the Profit and Loss Account, summarise performance at the end of the year.
2. Budgets are about the flow of cash into and out of the bank account. Financial statements deal in revenue and costs, which arise when invoices are generated. This can be a different point in time to bank transactions.
3. Trade credit is the most common reason why cash flow is different from revenue and cost timings. Consumers can be offered credit, especially in the retail industry (e.g. when purchasing furniture such as sofas).
4. Bad debts arise when a customer who is given credit doesn't pay the debt within the period of credit given.
5. Turnover is generally used to describe the revenue acquired over a full year of trading, e.g. a "one million pound turnover business". Sales revenue is used to describe income generated from sales on a daily, weekly or monthly basis. When businesses talk in terms of 'unit sales', they are referring to the number of units sold, rather than the financial value of those sales.
6. Variances are the difference between what was budgeted for and what actually happened. They can be favourable (i.e. revenue exceeded expectations or costs were below expectations); or they can be adverse (i.e. under-performed on revenue or over-spent on costs).

Now ask yourself:

1. What financial measures can be used to improve cash flow?

Now ask yourself (suggested answers):

1. **What financial measures can be used to improve cash flow?**

   a. Improved **trade credit terms** (i.e. ask suppliers for more time to pay or an increased credit limit)

   b. Better **credit control management** by preventing bad debts from arising.

   c. Arrange **short-term borrowing** through an overdraft facility or loan with the bank. A loan may have a lower interest rate than an overdraft, but would need to be paid back in fixed, regular instalments, whereas the overdraft would allow for less regular payments.

   d. **Debt factoring**, where an institution (e.g. a bank) effectively buys the sales invoices from the company. The business then receives cash (up to about 80% of the invoice value) from the factoring institution immediately. However, the customer then owes the factoring institution instead of the company. The final balance is paid to the company once the invoice is settled in full, less interest costs.

   e. **Sale and leaseback**. A company sells a major asset for cash, and then leases it back from the new owner.

CHAPTER 35

Josef and his amazing techni-organic dream coat

Two weeks later, we arrived in Prague and were taken to a wonderful hotel in the heart of the city.

The next day, Alex joined me on a trip to a textile manufacturer. The other two guests were assigned their own visits.

We arrived in a factory that was about ten miles outside of the city. A very amiable man greeted us, wearing a bushy moustache and braces. His name was Josef, and he was the factory manager.

He first took us on a tour of the factory. His English was very good as he had spent three years living in Devon in his early twenties. He now looked to be in his fifties.

I asked him why he had gone to live in Devon. He said a wise man in his village once told him that the girls from Devon were the most attractive of anywhere in the world. So he saved up and left his home for Devon, to meet his wife. He found her after a year and then they returned to the Czech Republic. He said she was indeed the most attractive girl in the world. Her name is Susan and they are still together now. She helps him run the factory and was joining us for coffee, once she returned from an errand to the bank.

His factory was the most advanced in the Czech Republic for textiles. The whole building was electronically programmed, which meant they were able to measure and control everything, from moisture levels to temperature. This improved their quality control and also the efficiency of production.

He got very excited when he showed us the different fabrics they used. I mentioned my wish for wrinkle free cotton and he pulled a huge face.

"No, no, no. You should not use these fabrics."

"Why?" I asked nervously.

"These fabrics are very bad for our health. Formaldehyde. Have you heard of that? Maker of such material use this chemical in their treatment. It is very dangerous."

I looked alarmingly at Alex and he looked back at me. "I wasn't aware of this," I told Josef.

"Think about it like this. We all wear clothing every day. Well, except for naturists. They have the right idea. But you get arrested for that, no?! Anyway, we put these fabrics next to our bodies every day. This means every day we are exposed to whatever chemicals go into these fabrics. But we don't think of that. We only think of the food we consume and the air we breathe."

"But surely any chemicals used in production have disappeared by the time they reach us?"

"Well, that is the risk we all take. Formaldehyde is a very dangerous substance. This is correct. We know this. I don't think it is so easy to assume that it just disappears when it reaches the home. Absolutely not. But it is not just us. We must think of the people in the third world who must work with these dangerous chemicals every day. Thousands die each year. They earn very little money and spend maybe sixteen hours each day in contact with these chemicals."

"So, do you use these fabrics here?"

"Absolutely not. We only use organic fabrics. That is why we are the most respected textile factory in the whole of Czech Republic. Come, I show you."

He took out a small roll of fabric from under a desk. "This is organic cotton. It is beautiful, no? This has come all the way from India. There are no pesticides used in the making of this cotton. It is all made using bugs and natural repellents. The farmers are happy and we are wearing a garment that is healthy." He pulled gently on his shirt.

Then he introduced us to some of the workers in his factory. What surprised me was that all the workers wore different coloured shirts according to where they were in the factory. And there were interconnected panels of lights above the workspaces with cords coming down.

"You are very observant noticing the lights and cords, young Lucinda," said Josef with a smile. "This is called *andon*. It is our commitment to continuous improvement. Whenever there is a problem with a machine, the worker pulls the cord. This stops production in the *kaizen* group and all the workers come together to fix the problem."

"What is that word? Kaizen?"

"Yes. It is Japanese. They introduced the world to *quality assurance* many years ago and now we have all adopted it, even here in little Czech Republic. You are familiar with Quality Assurance, right?" He continued before Alex could answer. "It basically means we pay attention all the time to every little detail, to make sure every garment is perfect. So the workers in an area of the factory are part of a kaizen group. They form the ideas on improving production and they pass those ideas on."

"But if everyone stops work as soon as there is a problem, aren't you wasting time by getting them all to stop work?"

"What is the point of them working if there is a bottleneck in the process? We use the Theory of Constraints to concentrate the right amount of effort in each part of the process. This ensures production is continuous. The moment production stops, it creates a bottleneck. We need to fix that problem as quickly as possible to ensure everyone can work."

"Your factory seems to be laid out in a particular way?" asked Alex. "Is this to minimise distance travelled?"

"Of course," said Josef. "And you know the great thing? We pass these savings on to the customer. We quote a particular price. If we can fulfil that order with less expense than we expected, then we give a little of that saving back to the customer in the form of a discount."

"And if it takes longer than you expected?"

"Then we bear the full cost of this. The customer is not to blame for our poor performance. But it doesn't happen very often, because we are very good at what we do!"

"It's very unusual to discount like that," said Alex.

"Yes, I suppose it is. But we take the view that the customer is part of our business. So they should benefit if we perform well. And you know what? We have fantastic repeat business. Once a customer uses us, they always stay. Often, they send more of their production to us and we find it difficult to cope. That is why we don't need to advertise for business. We grow by getting more and more business from our existing customers." I thought back to Brita.

"Was it always like this?" asked Alex.

"Not at all. Five years ago, the company was nearly bankrupt. So the owner, a great local man called Pavel, had to fire the manager. He said he cried the night he did this because he had been a loyal worker for ten years. But he had little idea how to run a factory.

"When he hired me, he told me I had six months to turn it around or the factory would be forced to close. Dear old Pavel was bankrolling it with his own money. Quality control was very poor. Because nobody was checking the finished garments against the agreed standard, the company was getting lots of rejected orders. They would be forced to re-run them or face legal action. And back then, labour productivity was very bad. Very bad." He shook his head gravely. "We measured it by the number of units made by each employee, over one day. At the time, we had exactly fifty employees and we averaged around 2,000 units per day. So divide 2,000 by 50 and you have…?"

"Forty," said Alex.

"Correct. Each employee would make 40 units per day. On average. That was our labour productivity. Do you know what our labour productivity is today?"

"Sixty?" I asked, as a random guess.

"Come. I show you." He led us to a little computer screen and after a few clicks brought up a page with a number of graphs on it. "This is our performance dashboard. It shows us each day how well we are doing. See this here?" He pointed at a particular line graph. "This is our labour productivity for the last ten working days. It is never below 85. That is the number we need to hit to ensure we meet our required level of profit. In any order where we go above the magic level, we give half back to the customer as a discount and keep half for ourselves."

"So, you've doubled productivity in five years?" I asked.

"We doubled it in one year, my dear. For the last four years, we have made great profits. And of course Pavel, he is very happy with this. He doesn't have to eat bread and water every day! But so are the workers. We now employ over 80 people. They get a handsome bonus every Christmas for their performance. So they are very happy. And we have done it all by putting quality first. Which means working towards zero defects. Last month, we achieved it for a whole week. One day soon, we do it for a whole month."

We enjoyed a wonderful lunch with Josef and his wife Susan. They were both lovely and told us lots of stories about the Czech Republic and the factory. Later that day, Alex and I were sat in the bar at the hotel, talking enthusiastically about the day.

"You know, I think it's changed my mind about the duvet covers I want to produce," I said. "I'm not so sure I am doing the right thing by trying to make products easy to iron, if they are doing so much damage to other people and maybe even the people who lie in bed underneath them?"

"There is an argument to say that's just the way of the world. Chemicals do a lot of good in many ways. And so long as companies who use them are responsible about how they use them, then, why should we worry? It is not our fault. And at the end of the day, a company needs to make a profit to keep its workers in a job."

"But Josef's factory is keeping people in a job without putting other people at risk! He has a social conscience. After seeing and hearing what I've seen today, I'm not sure I want to support a world that doesn't have a social conscience."

"Do you feel that strongly about it?"

"God yes! Don't you?" I felt alarmed that Alex didn't seem to be quite as bothered as I was.

"Yes I do. But you need to consider *market conditions*."

"Market conditions? What does that mean?"

"Well, it means considering what the industry you are operating in does. You need to be competitive, remember. If it costs twice the price to make an organic duvet set, will there be a market for it? Your business objective is to make a profit, at the end of the day."

"Well, maybe my business objective is wrong then? Is making a profit at the expense of others ethically right? I'm not sure it is. And it's pretty clear Josef doesn't think it is and look how well they're doing."

"I'm not arguing with you, Lu. I'm just playing devil's advocate. And I want you to succeed."

"Yes I know. But the fact I fundamentally disagree with what you are saying means that I probably need to re-think what sort of business I want to create. I need to research how bad this textile problem is in the third world. And if it's as bad as Josef says it is, then maybe I need to help do something about it."

"But it's like the issue of going vegetarian. One person going vegetarian won't change things and if, in the unlikely event that we were all vegetarian one day, none of these animals would exist and the world wouldn't cope with the increased demand for fruit and vegetables."

"If everyone took the view that their individual actions cannot change things, then nothing would ever change. Sometimes, you have to do the right thing, irrespective of what everyone else does."

We carried on debating our clearly different points of view and then had dinner with the other guys. They seemed to have had good days too. Then Alex walked me to my room. We kissed outside and said goodnight. I went inside and stood by the door for a while, wondering if I should go back out and invite him in. I resisted the urge and went to bed. He texted me a lovely good night message and I sent him an emoji kiss back.

What you've covered:

Theme	Amplification
Operations Management	What is meant by continuous improvement including concepts such as kaizen and andon
Quality	What is meant by quality and why is it important in business?
Quality	The difference between quality control and quality assurance
Ethics	The ethical issues businesses face, such as the treatment of workers
Ethics	The meaning of corporate social responsibility
PESTLE: Environmental	Some of the environmental issues in business
Productivity	How to calculate labour productivity

Memory hook: Josef and his amazing techni-organic dream coat

Josef believes in the use of organic fabrics to combat the potential dangers of chemicals. He has built his factory around the premise of *doing the right thing*. This means operating ethically, which includes sharing profits with customers, respecting the safety of workers and focusing upon quality and good practice. This, in turn, helps to make the business financially sustainable, which helps to protect their jobs.

So, key points to remember:

1. Continuous improvement is within the concept of *Total Quality Management* (TQM), which means everyone within an organisation is committed to an on-going process of improvement.
2. Kaizen and Andon are two techniques used within TQM. Kaizen means working in groups to improve. Andon is a cord system used to stop production whenever a problem arises.
3. Quality control means ensuring that every item produced or served is consistent with the specification through rigorous checks and inspections. Quality assurance means looking at every stage of the process to ensure everything is done correctly.
4. *Lean management* is an area of TQM that is focused upon minimising waste and maximising efficiency.
5. Labour productivity = Total output / Number of employees

Now ask yourself:

1. What do Philip Crosby's Four Absolutes of Quality refer to?
2. How would Total Quality Management be relevant in a service organisation, such as a hotel?

Now ask yourself (suggested answers):

1. **What do Philip Crosby's Four Absolutes of Quality refer to?**
   i. Quality is about **conforming to requirements**. E.g. if someone asks you to wash a car, the requirement is that it is totally clean afterwards.
   ii. **Preventing defects** happening is better than correcting mistakes, i.e. quality assurance is preferable to quality control. (Remember ABC: Assurance Beats Control).
   iii. The aim is **zero defects**. To achieve this, you need continuous improvement, i.e. practice makes perfect.
   iv. The **cost of achieving quality** is less than the cost of not achieving quality. E.g. recall how Pavel's factory was forced to re-make bad batches for dissatisfied customers. Had they improved quality in the first place, this wouldn't have arisen.

2. **How would Total Quality Management be relevant in a service organisation, such as a hotel?**

   To answer this, we need to address the differences between the manufacturing industries, where TQM has its foundation, and the service industry, which is not product based. In particular:

   ▪ In a hotel, work is performed for someone else – the customer. Within a manufacturing plant, work is performed for other members of the assembly process.
   ▪ Manufactured products are tangible, such as a perfectly assembled car, whereas the service industry deals in intangibles, such as a customer's degree of satisfaction. TQM is about measurement, which is possible in the physical world, but less easy in the non-physical world.
   ▪ The service industry primarily focuses upon the customer. The mood of the customer will vary, often through no fault of the hotel. Also, different customers have different expectation levels. This means 'zero defects' might never be achievable, no matter how good the hotel is, because some customers will always find fault. Manufacturing is based around making one identical product.
   ▪ The service industry is heavily focused on timeliness. Yet the completion of a task is often outside the control of the employee.

For example, if a hotel receptionist is dealing with one customer, other customers in the queue will be kept waiting. The receptionist is obliged to resolve the issue with the current customer, but in doing so, is dissatisfying others.

- The customer is frequently involved in the delivery of the service and as such introduces an unknown and unpredictable influence on the process. Can the hotel be at fault if the customer floods the bathroom, which drips into the room of the guest below? The customer also adds uncertainty to the process, because it is often difficult to determine their exact requirements and what they regard as an acceptable standard of service.

CHAPTER 36

Pizza go home

I spent most of the next day sightseeing around Prague by myself. Alex had to accompany one of the other guys on their trade mission. I ambled through the streets and enjoyed the sense of freedom that being in a city with no particular place to go offers you. I saw a number of fast food outlets called *Paneria*, so decided I really needed to try one. Feeling healthy, I had a fresh salad, which was really good.

Prices seemed to be pretty much in line with the UK. At least, that was my finding in the multitude of clothes shops I visited! I came across a takeaway pizza company that described their service in English. However, its translation was highly amusing! Later in the trip, Alex and I walked past it again, so we got a passer by to take a photo!

Then, I stopped off at a local coffee shop and got chatting to an elderly man who recognised my English accent. He asked me how I was enjoying Prague and I made the mistake of asking him how he was doing. He proceeded to rant about the economic situation. He was particularly annoyed about the interest rates of the country. Apparently, they have dropped to almost zero, for the first time he could remember. This was bad for him because he had savings that were earning no interest. But his son was an electrician and it was good for him because he'd secured a business loan on very good terms. He asked me what the interest rate was in the UK and I guessed it to be about two percent. I reminded myself to check later, in case I ever got asked this question again. My coffee was downed quickly and I made my escape.

In the evening, we were all invited to an ambassador's reception. It turned out there were a number of other British trade missions taking place that week and we were all brought together for a celebration. The Ambassador was a fairly senior British government official who was based in Prague to support British expatriates and represent the UK in various matters.

He delivered an interesting speech, explaining how important it was for the UK to conduct business with the Czech Republic. He talked it up as a developing and prosperous country that had always enjoyed good ties with Britain.

Later on, I chatted to the man who was trying to progress his dog kennel idea. He was a pleasant but slightly eccentric guy called Dennis. As he explained his idea, it became clear that this was no ordinary kennel! It was more like a miniature house. So when the dog walked on a mat outside the kennel, the door opened outwards. The door then shut automatically, once the dog went inside.

I asked what I thought was a fairly obvious question. How did the dog get out once inside? He said the kennel door would open as soon as the dog barked. Assuming he was being serious, I asked what happens if the dog wants to get out, but doesn't know he has to bark. In fact, another pressure plate on the inside would activate the door, once the dog needed to get out. Another unusual feature was that the kennel would light up once the dog was inside.

Somehow I couldn't see him faring terribly well on Dragon's Den with this. I had visions of hundreds of trapped dogs inside his kennels, unable to figure out its exit strategy. It reminded me of the poor translation for takeaway pizza earlier that day – Dennis assumed dogs would understand the concept of his kennel, even though they didn't speak 'human'! I wondered whether there was any evidence dogs actually need this kind of elaborate housing, but didn't want to appear too negative.

Just as I thought I was escaping Dennis, Alex came over and joined us. He had gone back with him to the factory earlier that day.

"So, I thought it went well today, Dennis. Are you pleased?" Dennis had the look of someone who would never be pleased. I decided right there that if Dennis was canine, he would be a bulldog.

"Pretty good, yeah," he replied.

They had discussed the feasibility of Dennis's design at length with the factory engineer. I guessed that was the bit about how to get the dogs out of the kennel without giving them anxiety attacks. He said they had spoken about inventory too. This got me interested, as it was a key question for me too, particularly after meeting Josef yesterday.

"So, how many kennels do you plan to make?" I asked.

"Confidentially, the target is to sell 500 kennels in the first year. But I couldn't find a manufacturer back home able to do this within my budget. I looked into South East Asia, but they were talking big numbers and the shipping time wasn't helpful. So this company today provides a realistic solution for me."

"That's really interesting because I have a similar issue with my product." My confidence to talk in this way with other business people was growing. "I want to do a kind of just-in-time model whilst holding small batches of stock."

Dennis nodded vociferously. "Yeah, the maximum order quantity I can financially work with is a hundred. These people today can take re-orders in units of a hundred and provide a fairly short lead-time. So, from the time I place an order, they could ship me a batch of kennels within five working days. And the land freight time to the UK is something like 48 hours, so in seven days I will have a whole new batch. That's great for my cash flow because I can go pretty close to zero-inventory before re-ordering. The one thing they won't do is offer credit until at least one year of trading."

"So you can't buy now, pay later?"

"Nope. Not until one year. And even then, they will only offer me something like seven days. They clearly have fairly challenging cash flow too. But at this re-order level, I can cope with that because I'll have recovered all my costs from the last batch of sales."

"That's really good," I said. "It's got me wondering whether the factory owner I met today could work on a similar principle."

"Well, definitely speak to them. It seems like they really want to do business with us, which is great. I went to South Africa on one of these trade missions about three years ago, and the people I met then didn't seem bothered."

"Was that with the dog kennel?" I asked, with a concealed degree of empathy for the South Africans.

"No, that was a different venture. I sold some of the assets in that business to finance the R&D for this."

"So, will you be fully self-financed with *Home Dog*?" asked Alex. I guessed that was the name for his product. 'Dog Go Home' would be more appropriate, I thought to myself.

"I had interest from a venture capitalist guy. But I was a bit uneasy about giving him too much of a stake. I was looking for a fairly hands-off investor, but he seemed to really want to get involved." Probably because he could see how nuts it was to have a dog trapped in a kennel, I thought.

"I've launched a crowdfunding page. So far, that's doing OK, but it's a little short on target. I'm focusing on dog owners obviously. Does either of you two own a dog?"

I shook my head. "Sadly not," added Alex.

"That's a shame, said Dennis. "You could have added to the pot! I also have a bank loan offer to fall back on, but I much prefer the crowdfunding approach, because my investors are effectively my initial marketing channel through word of mouth."

"Did you get a good interest rate on your loan?" I asked, suddenly thinking back to the guy in the coffee shop that afternoon.

"I think about 5%. The standard sort of rate really."

At this point, the Ambassador joined us and Dennis proceeded to repeat his story of the day. The Ambassador was very polite and listened intently.

Alex and I made a swift getaway and we moved out onto the veranda, overlooking Charles Bridge. He gave me a quick kiss, which I thought was very brave, as it could have been seen by any of the guests.

"Aren't we meant to be here as 'associates'?" I asked teasingly.

"I couldn't resist," he replied. "You look gorgeous tonight. And I was thinking about what you said about only inviting you on business dates. Right now, I'd give anything not to be here on business with you."

"Well, we've got tomorrow night to ourselves, haven't we? Maybe you could take me out on a proper date? No business meetings. No big talks on quality assurance. Just quality time."

"Sounds amazing. I'll plan a nice surprise for you."

"It doesn't involve meeting ex-girlfriends who make t-shirts in Prague does it?"

"Well actually..." I kicked him in his shin. A little too hard.

"That was for t-shirt Sam," I said. "Now we're even!"

What you've covered:

Theme	Amplification
Interest rates	The impact of interest rates on business decisions
Economies of scale	The significance of economies of scale for small businesses
International trade	The factors around international trade
The European Union	The security that being part of the EU afforded the UK

Memory hook: Pizza go home

Dennis' kennel idea is about as lost in translation for dogs as 'Pizza Go Home' was. It serves as a memory hook for a number of issues relating to trading internationally. In particular, he was able to work with the Czech Republic much more easily than South Asia. This raises a number of questions following the UK's decision to exit the European Union. For example, will British companies still be able to trade freely with countries within Europe, or will potential import/export duty and price rises make it more difficult?

So, key points to remember:

1. Low interest rates reduce the cost of borrowing money. However, people or businesses with savings accounts do not benefit, since the return they receive on their savings will be lower.
2. Purchasing large quantities of goods reduces the unit cost due to economies of scale. For many small businesses, however, holding a lot of stock is not realistic due to financial limitations. This means they are often forced to pay a premium for lower volume orders.
3. The European Union offers free trade between all of its member countries.
4. Being in the EU currently provides a free market for the import and export of goods between the UK and its other member states. As the UK leaves Europe, new trading relationships will need to be negotiated.

Now ask yourself:

1. What are the potential trading consequences for UK businesses following the decision to leave the EU?
2. What is the current base rate of interest within the UK and who sets it? Why is it lower than interest rates offered on loans and mortgages? And why do they vary so much?
3. What would be the consequences of a rise and fall in interest rates?

Now ask yourself (suggested answers):

1. **What are the potential trading consequences for UK business following the decision to leave the EU?**

   - **Tariffs** imposed by EU member governments on our businesses. However, the UK government could equally impose tariffs of its own. Furthermore, membership of the World Trade Organisation means that tariff arrangements cannot be imposed on selective countries, but not to others. This would override any decision taken by Europe on the UK.
   - **Product standards**. Currently, the UK must conform to product standards, as set by the EU. This includes things like labelling, packaging and levels of certain chemicals in foods or other produce. Leaving the EU will remove that conformity and businesses may incur costs in modifications made to these standards, for products entering the EU market.
   - **Service provision**. Once the UK has left the EU, a UK company providing services in other member countries may have to comply with the rules of a foreign regulatory authority.
   - The EU has negotiated a number of preferential trade agreements with other countries. On leaving the EU, the UK will have to negotiate its own **trade agreements**. This could benefit or penalise the UK import/export economy.

2. **What is the current base rate of interest within the UK and who sets it? Why is it lower than interest rates offered on loans and mortgages? And why do they vary so much?**

   The current base rate of interest (as of August 2016) is 0.25% and is set by the Bank of England's Monetary Policy Committee. Banks and other lenders have to charge a higher rate of interest than this in order to cover their costs and make a profit. Rates vary across institutions for a number of reasons, but in particular:

   a. To be competitive. Customers are likely to want to repay as little interest as possible.
   b. Economies of scale. Larger institutions can afford to be more competitive on rates.

c. Operational efficiency. If banks employ more staff than competitors, or hold more branches, then their costs will be higher and this will need to be reflected in their interest rates.

d. Levels of risk. Payday lenders charge very high rates of interest because they are typically lending money to people with poor credit histories. This means their likelihood of defaulting on repayments is much higher.

3. **What would be the consequences of a rise and fall in interest rates for businesses?**

A rise in interest rates:
- Raises the cost of borrowing for businesses – including business loans, overdraft facilities and leasing agreements.
- Typically leads to a rise in the value of the pound. This makes UK products less competitive overseas and may therefore lead to reduced international sales.
- Since customers needing to borrow are affected by a rise in interest rates, they are likely to consume less. Therefore, overall sales levels are likely to fall.
- Higher interest rates also increase the cost of government interest payments on its own debt. This could lead to higher taxes in the future, including corporation tax.
- Reduced confidence. A rise in interest rates makes people and businesses less willing to invest.

A fall in interest rates:
- The cost of borrowing will reduce. Therefore consumers should be more likely to spend and companies more likely to invest.
- The value of the pound should fall, which makes the UK more competitive and should lead to more international sales.
- The government will be more likely to lower taxes, since its own debt repayments will be lower.
- Increased consumer confidence.

The final day of the trade mission involved us all going to meet one of the Czech Republic's leading digital technology companies. The guy who was developing his own website was particularly interested in this and I sat next to him on the minibus taking us out there. His name was Keith.

"So, what exactly does your website do?" I asked.

"In a nutshell, it tracks luxury products around the world. And promotes them."

"Wow, that's exciting!" I said. "What sort of luxury products?"

"Anything really. Villas, Swiss watches, sports cars. Even yachts."

I was beginning to see a bit of a hitch to his idea but wasn't sure whether to say it, for fear of being too critical. In the end, I figured it best to do it tactfully.

"Do you think the people who can afford luxury stuff would actually buy these things online? I mean, wouldn't they go and buy from a shop, or even get their staff to buy for them?"

"Sure, but you know the really cool thing? I'm not actually selling to the rich and famous at all! In a nutshell, my site is kind of a stock market for cool luxury products. Do you know who are more interested in luxury products than anyone else? … The people who cannot afford any of it."

"Oh I see." Except, I didn't really see. I noticed he sounded a little bit American and had a habit of saying 'in a nutshell'. "So, you are purchasing these products, but nobody can afford to buy them from you?"

"E-tailing? Heck, I'm not retailing them! Some of the items we'll be tracking run into seven figures. The site will act as a kind of online magazine for the wannabe rich and famous."

"But if nobody can afford to buy any of the stuff you are tracking, how will you ever make any sales?"

"Through advertising products they can afford to buy, and need to if they want to be rich and famous. So: books on how to be an online millionaire, private singing lessons, football academies for their kids, modelling agencies, platinum credit cards. Things like that."

I was beginning to get really curious by his idea. It actually sounded quite brilliant, if slightly unethical. Was it possible to be retailing one thing, but promoting something entirely different? My mind was drifting back to the organic lifestyle thing.

"Everything is done through m-commerce," he said.

"What is m-commerce?" I asked, distracted from thinking his idea through.

"M-commerce is selling mainly through mobile phones. Pretty much all the people I need to reach will be accessing via their phone. That's why I want to see these folk today, because they specialise in m-commerce."

"So, do people need to join your site?"

"Absolutely! The trick is to make it seem difficult to break in, even if it isn't. They're effectively joining the rich club, even when they're not rich. Ask anyone who aspires to be rich to join a site that tracks stupidly expensive stuff and they'll jump through as many hoops as you put there. Those hoops help me to learn about their aspirations and stuff, which in turn influences which products I try selling to them. Although, I guess some of the people will just be learning about expensive stuff, so they can brag to their mates that they have it."

I was beginning to think that Keith didn't have too much respect for the people he was going to be selling to. I wasn't sure if that was a good place to be.

He continued. "I remember as a kid, these salesmen came around to my parents' house to sell them this fancy vacuum cleaner. They were there for hours, but my Dad was having none of it. Then they started showing me pictures of insects they had blown up to look gigantic and really scary, with claws and everything. It was like something out of a Stephen King book! When I saw them, I begged by Mom to buy one, so we could get rid of these bugs they told me were in my bed. Only their vacuum cleaner would remove them. That's kind of stuck with me all my life. The person you try to convince to buy something isn't always the person who actually buys it. Toy shops use this strategy all the time."

I suspected this childhood trauma had inadvertently rubbed off on Keith. He was the modern day equivalent of those vacuum salesmen. Just as I was about to respond, we pulled up outside our destination.

We entered their building and it was totally cool. All of the doors opened automatically and everything seemed slightly futuristic. It even had a giant waterfall in reception.

We went through to a meeting room where they had laid out coffee and healthy juice. I helped myself to a dark red juice made with berries.

A lady called Veronika introduced herself and gave us a history of the company through a presentation. It was designed so professionally. Later, Alex told me she was using a package called Prezi. She spoke word perfect English.

We were invited to share our business ideas and Keith immediately introduced his. Veronika listened intently to his description and then fed back her opinion.

"So, my advice would be to populate the site with lots of beautiful images and maybe some video. Make the homepage an image of a beautiful man and woman, like something from a perfume advert. And keep it minimalist, because that's what luxury needs to project."

Keith was nodding in agreement. "What platform would you recommend?"

"Well, based on what you've said, I would guess you are looking omni-channel? The market leader is Magento. We have our own bespoke platform that I can discuss with you later, if you wish. But if you want to go alone, Magento would work well."

I wanted to ask Alex what omni-channel meant, but I didn't want to whisper, so I made a note to ask him later. Turns out it means selling across different retailers.

"Then use digital marketing techniques to truly understand each member. That way you can personalise what they see accordingly," continued Veronika. "Build relationships by getting to know them as individuals. And of course, try to get dialogues going between members so they effectively do the hard work for you by creating reviews and comments."

Dennis introduced his kennel idea and Veronika provided him with some tips. Then she asked me directly what my idea was.

"I'm looking at selling a special kind of bedding," I replied.

"OK. So you'll be needing to convey a sense of relaxation," said Veronika. "You need people to imagine what it would be like under your bedding." I sensed a ripple of amusement amongst Keith and Dennis.

"But how do I do that on a website?"

"Through the use of neutral colours and a feeling of serenity. Visit some sites selling holistic therapies and you'll get an idea of the thing I mean. Will you be designing your own website?"

"Definitely not," I said. "I wouldn't have a clue where to start!"

"So, when you source the right provider, make sure you include in your brief the need to reflect peace and tranquility. But they'll probably understand that anyway. The task of online now is to replicate the feeling of what it's like there for real. So, for your luxury brands website Keith, some video of a sporty person riding an electronic surfboard. That kind of thing."

She gave us a tour of the building and introduced us to some of her designers. I imagined how great it would be to have them create my website, so I decided to ask. She didn't want to give a figure in case it was misleading, so handed me a business card and asked me to get in touch with my needs and she would price something up.

That evening was my date with Alex. I wore my favourite dress and he looked amazing in a casual jacket. We were taken to a restaurant by taxi.

The meal was fantastic. We talked about all sorts of things and never strayed into the subject of business, even though I was dying to ask him whether I should use Josef's factory to make my products and Veronika's digital marketing company. We talked about our childhoods. It was a bit painful for him because his parents separated when he was young. But he still sees both of them now and is close to his step-sister Amy.

And after? Well, we arrived outside my hotel room again. He told me his shin was still bruised from my kick the night before and asked if I could rub it better. I told him to be careful, or I'd kick the other one!

What you've covered:

Theme	Amplification
Digital marketing	The role of digital marketing in building customer relationships
Digital marketing	Digital marketing terms such as e-tailing and m-commerce
Business psychology	Recognition of how businesses need to understand customers' needs and behaviours
Business psychology	The use of aspirational lifestyle scenarios to influence people to buy 'enabling' products
Sales techniques	The use of influencers to persuade the purse holder.

Memory hook: Rags to riches

This chapter uses Keith's website idea to introduce some of the psychology and sales tactics used in business. For example, his website is promoting products that his members cannot afford to buy, in order to sell them a 'gateway' or 'enabling' product to the lifestyle they desire. This is tapping into the psyche of his potential customers and using digital marketing to build relationships amongst them.

So, key points to remember:

1. The products a website are promoting are not always what are being sold. Many websites tap into aspiration and lifestyle persuading visitors to buy products they perceive they need, in order to achieve their ambitions. This is common in the health and beauty retail sector.
2. The influencer is not always the purse/wallet holder. Toyshops take advantage of this all the time.
3. E-commerce is the buying and selling of products through electronic channels, such as website and social media sites.
4. M-tailing is about promoting and selling products and services through mobile devices.

Now ask yourself:

1. How do early adopters of technology benefit the company that is developing it?

Now ask yourself (suggested answers):

1. How do early adopters of technology benefit the company that is developing it?

   - Giving product reviews
   - Developing online dialogue and PR
   - Providing product feedback to refine further development.

CHAPTER 38

Fast forward

So, fast-forward two years and things have moved on somewhat!

I took the internship with Orchid Marketing. Whilst there, I studied for a qualification in marketing, which I passed with a distinction.

I stayed close to Comedy Will and used my newly acquired expertise in marketing to help him promote his website. It has continued to grow and he's now left his job to manage that and a couple of other digital ventures full-time. He made me a partner in the company, so I get a small salary for my efforts and more free comedy nights than I know what do with. I sometimes feel like an agent to the stars and have met lots of celebrity comedians through it!

And the other businesses I was introduced to? Well the hoverboard thing still hasn't quite taken off. It seems like there's a lot more technical work to do on that, so I don't expect to see any of you hoverboarding in the near future. I think Brad now does some engineering consultancy work in the South of France.

The Second Life project went from strength to strength. They've now rolled it out to several more centres in other parts of the country. Philippa oversees them all. I believe she has also moved into politics, so I expect her to one day become Britain's third female Prime Minister. Although probably for a different party!

Mum took redundancy from the council and has found a new job in a training company. She loves every bit of it: much more job security and no crazy women stealing from the till! It turns out my suspicions on her dating *rendezvous*, back where this story started, were totally correct. Although, it was somewhat of a surprise when she revealed it was none other than Jack, her trade union representative from work! He's now a permanent fixture in our lives. Apart from his cheesy jokes, he's OK!

Uncle Steve turned down the chance to buy his competitor and now has a five-year exit strategy, whereupon they will retire to the Algarve. Or rather, Aunt Kath is going to the Algarve, with or without him!

As for all the entrepreneurs and companies I met in Prague? Well, I can't say I've heard too much about Dennis's dog kennels. Nor have I found Keith's website. But I do know that Josef's factory is doing well and I'm sure Veronika is still wowing the world of digital marketing. Like everyone else, I have no idea where Brexit is going to leave the UK. No doubt it will be an important few years in our economic history…

As for Alex? Well, I still see him just about every day as we're now engaged. It turns out he wasn't quite the lothario I suspected after the t-shirt Sam episode. I do keep a keen eye on him, although not quite so keen as Sam did!

And last but not least…*Duvet Days*? Well, I reduced my hours at Orchid Marketing and managed to get it up and running last year. 'Touch wood', it's still going strong. I've developed a little network of local seamstresses who supply me with orders on a small batch basis. We have a loyal but growing following. We managed to return a profit in our first year of operation, which I now realise, was a fantastic achievement!

However, my real passion is teaching! I have started to deliver some courses for the careers service at the university and also at a local further education college. I teach entrepreneurship and marketing. I love the buzz of seeing people explore ideas of their own. Hopefully my classes will inspire some of them to do something different with their lives also. I really believe that we are entering a new age of business start-up, which may well be just what Brexit needs to help us get through it stronger.

So, that's about it. I hope my story has inspired you to think about business differently? Maybe it's inspired you to start your own business one day? I can't pretend it was easy, but it's certainly been interesting!

Index

J

Jamie Oliver, 59
Jo Malone, 5, 6
job design, 268
job enlargement, 269
job enrichment, 269
job processing, 188
job rotation, 106, 269
job share, 50, 101, 102, 105
John Lewis, 64, 76, 171
just-in-time, 185, 188, 315

K

Kaizen, 303, 309
KFC, 15
Kurt Lewin, 146, 150

L

labour productivity, 49, 304, 305, 308
lead-time, 185, 188, 315
lean management, 309
limited company, 59, 60, 62, 64, 69, 196, 279, 280
limited partnership, 59
loan capital, 276, 279
loss leader, 202

M

macro economy, 128
Malcolm Gladwell, 75
manufacturing, 42, 310
margin, 14, 42, 193, 199, 200, 201, 235, 238, 260, 275
margin of safety, 200
Mark Zuckerberg, 5, 6
market conditions, 306
market orientation, 250
market research, 9, 12, 13, 226
market share, 166
market size, 166
marketing mix, 248, 253, 256, 266
Marks & Spencer, 89, 290
mark-up, 113, 193
Maslow's Hierarchy of Needs, 264
mass marketing, 42, 250
mass production, 188
m-commerce, 324, 328

Mercedes-Benz, 126, 290
micro economy, 128, 130
micro-business, 98
Microsoft, 251
Minecraft, 31
motivation theories, 267
m-tailing, 328
multi-national corporations, 95
municipal services, 52
mutual businesses, 58, 171

N

National Health Service, 52, 54
national insurance, 55
net present value, 281
niche market, 37, 75, 85
niche marketing, 250
non-current asset, 238
non-financial methods of motivation, 267
Non-Governmental Organisation, 141
not-for-profit sector, 58, 62, 173

O

oligopoly, 131, 132
omni-channel, 326
operating profit, 196, 197, 200, 232, 233, 235, 239, 275
operational decisions, 280
operations management, 42
opportunity cost, 238
organic agriculture, 89
organisational structure, 50
outsourcing, 52
overtrading, 295

P

part-time working, 105
patent, 11, 13, 15, 26, 27, 205
payback period, 281
payday lenders, 321
peer-to-peer lending, 87
penetration pricing, 260
performance related pay, 268
perishable goods, 202
pharmaceuticals, 210
Philip Crosby, 309
piece rate, 268
pivoting, 120, 121
Premium Bonds, 54

Made in the USA
Charleston, SC
18 October 2016